THE PAST REDISCOVERED: FRENCH PAINTING 1800–1900

THE MINNEAPOLIS INSTITUTE OF ARTS
MINNEAPOLIS, MINNESOTA
JULY 3—SEPTEMBER 7, 1969

Exhibition Staff:

SAMUEL SACHS II, *chief curator, in charge of exhibition*

INEZ M. QUINN, *registrar*

BARBARA SHISSLER, *editor*

RUTH DEAN, *designer*

ELLEN BRADBURY, *research assistant*

MARGARET OLSON AND KAREN MacDONALD, *editorial assistants*

ANTHONY M. CLARK, *director, The Minneapolis Institute of Arts*

THIS EXHIBITION IS
UNDER THE HIGH PATRONAGE OF

HIS EXCELLENCY THE AMBASSADOR OF FRANCE
TO THE UNITED STATES AND MADAME CHARLES LUCET

THE MINISTRY OF CULTURE OF FRANCE

THE CULTURAL COUNSELOR TO THE FRENCH EMBASSY
AND MADAME ÉDOUARD MOROT-SIR

THE CONSUL-GENERAL OF FRANCE AT CHICAGO
AND MADAME JEAN-LOUIS MANDEREAU

THE GOVERNOR OF THE STATE OF MINNESOTA
AND MRS. HAROLD LeVANDER

THE HONORARY CONSUL FOR FRANCE AT MINNEAPOLIS
AND MRS. PHILIP W. PILLSBURY

THIS EXHIBITION IS
A BENEFACTION OF THE DAYTON CORPORATION FOUNDATION

LENDERS

Anonymous Lenders
Mr. and Mrs. Arthur G. Altschul, New York
Albright-Knox Art Gallery, Buffalo
Musée des Beaux-Arts, Bourdeaux
Museum of Fine Arts, Boston
Musée Municipal, Brest
National Gallery of Canada, Ottawa
Musée Carnavalet, Paris
Art Institute of Chicago, Chicago
Chrysler Art Museum, Provincetown
Mr. Walter P. Chrysler, Jr., New York
The Cleveland Museum of Art, Cleveland
Cummer Gallery of Art, Jacksonville
Dordrechts Museum, Dordrecht
Museum voor Schone Kunsten, Ghent
Musée Granet, Aix-en-Provence
The Honorable and Mrs. W. Averell Harriman, New York
Musée Thomas Henry, Cherbourg
Mr. J. Jerome Hill, New York
Musée Ingres, Montauban
Jeu de Paume, Paris
Mr. Cecil D. Kaufmann, Washington
Staatliche Kunsthalle, Karlsruhe
Musée du Louvre, Paris
Musée des Beaux-Arts, Marseille
Mr. and Mrs. Jean Mauzé, New York
Metropolitan Museum of Art, New York
Museum of Modern Art, New York
California Palace of the Legion of Honor, San Francisco
Musée Petit Palais, Paris
Philadelphia Museum of Art, Philadelphia
Rhode Island School of Design, Providence
Mr. and Mrs. Thibaut de St. Phalle, New York
Mr. and Mrs. David T. Schiff, New York
The National Gallery of Scotland, Edinburgh
Mr. and Mrs. Germain Seligman, New York
Smith College Museum of Art, Northampton
Taft Museum, Cincinnati
Toledo Museum of Art, Toledo
Miss Alice Tully, New York
Musée des Beaux-Arts, Valenciennes
M. Roger Varenne, Geneva
Musée National de Versailles, Versailles
Wadsworth Atheneum, Hartford
Walters Art Gallery, Baltimore
Mr. and Mrs. John Hay Whitney, New York
Yale University Art Gallery, New Haven

CONTENTS

FOREWORD

A l'Institut d'Art de Minneapolis, l'un des grands centres culturels des Etats-Unis, à son directeur et ses collaborateurs, j'adresse mes très sincères et cordiales félicitations, pour avoir choisi de présenter cette exposition qui, dans sa variété et sa richesse, donne une image représentative de la peinture française du XIXième siècle.

Attirés par la diversité des écoles qui se sont succédées dans un extraordinaire tumulte, nous oublions parfois la merveilleuse unité et la grande leçon de ce siècle qui est sorti d'une Révolution, l'une des plus fortes secousses de l'histoire, et qui a fini dans les lueurs tragiques de la première guerre mondiale. Le XIXième siècle a été le siècle de l'Homme. Il a cru en la liberté de l'individu; il a cru au génie, au peuple, à un nouvel univers. Il a eu le goût de l'exotisme et de l'aventure. Il a découvert la grandeur et l'originalité des cultures. Il a libéré, dans un immense souffle révolutionnaire, l'âme des nationalités. Nouveau Prométhée, il a cru au progrès servi par la science et l'industrie. Héroïque, combatif, et angoissé, emporté par une ivresse créatrice qui s'est répercutée de génération en génération, il a été visionnaire.

Il a renouvelé le visage universel de la France, qui est ainsi devenue le lieu de rencontre de toutes les recherches esthétiques. En luttant contre la tradition de l'Ecole et contre des techniques rigides, il a donné à l'artiste une nouvelle mission. La peinture est alors l'expression d'une étonnante expansion lyrique. Le tableau est espace en mouvement; grâce à de profonds changements dans la technique picturale, il révèle les mystères de l'air et de la lumière, le jeu infini et l'intimité de la couleur. Ce dynamisme, qui est l'essence de notre romantisme, introduit le miracle et la beauté dans la vie quotidienne des êtres et des objets. Il est la recherche d'un équilibre de l'homme pour qui l'art devient, de décor splendide qu'il était, confiance, dialogue, rayonnement. Telle est l'exceptionnelle leçon de cette exposition d'art français du XIXième siècle. Elle prouve que, dans cette éclatante aurore des temps modernes, la France a participé, avec son génie propre, à l'effort le plus grand que l'homme ait jamais tenté pour donner un sens nouveau à son destin et à sa puissance créatrice.

CHARLES LUCET,
Ambassadeur de France aux États-Unis

PREFACE

This exhibition offers the possibility of examining French 19th-century painting in fine, even notoriously great, examples. The principle of selection has been not theme, not insurance value, not familiarity, but quality. Quality can edify and inspire; in this exhibition we hope we have derived from quality not only pleasure but coverage. For, while the most famous artists of the period are present (sometimes in varied examples), the lesser or forgotten artists are too — inclusions demanded by the new bright eyes of collectors and students, quality having sparked shrewdness and sense. We can also claim that the coverage is more realistic than has been possible before. Moral or revolutionary reasons for liking a Manet and disliking a Bouguereau (or vice versa) seem finally outdated. There are considerable reasons — aside from popular taste — to admire what can be used from each of the old warring factions, and to reveal a more rich and sensible history of the proudest century of French painting.

It was not possible to get all that was needed. Both supervalued Impressionists and underconserved Academics mean intense difficulties to a lender: the special generosity and complex sacrifices of the private and public lenders to this exhibition have been extraordinary and are matters of profound gratitude.

Special gratitude is due to M. Edouard Morot-Sir, Le Conseiller Culturel, Ambassade de France, Representative of French Universities in the United States; M. Hubert Landais, Le Directeur des Musées de France, Administrateur de la Réunion des Musées Nationaux; M. Pierre Quoniam, Inspecteur général des Musées de Province; M. Michel Laclotte, Conservateur en Chef du Department des Peintures, Musée du Louvre; Professors Robert Rosenblum, Francis Haskell, John Maxon, and John Rewald; Mme D. Demetz; and M. Jean Lacambre. That this exhibition occurs or has merit is due to the supreme efforts of my colleague Samuel Sachs II, who has usually, and uniquely, been able to surmount even the worst difficulties.

This exhibition was made possible and is supported by a benefaction of the Dayton Corporation Foundation. The noble purpose of this benefaction is the establishment in the Twin Cities of an art exhibition of major prominence, lasting several months during the attractive Minnesota Summer, and helping to develop an appropriate, important cultural season for this area.

ANTHONY M. CLARK, *Director*

THE NINETEENTH-CENTURY FRANC REVALUED

The history of 19th-century French painting used to look quite tidy. There was a sequence of great *isms* (from Neo-Classicism to Post-Impressionism), a sequence of great artists (from David to Cézanne), and a sequence of moral victories in which truth, in the form of a Delacroix, a Monet, or a Gauguin, ultimately triumphed over the falsehood of the artistic establishment. But today, in 1969, this linear history and this dramatic parable of the battle of aesthetic good and evil no longer satisfy the curious historian and the adventurous spectator. More and more detached from the passions that used to be aroused by the championing of the origins of the modernist tradition, we can begin to relax and to re-examine the vast and unwieldy pictorial heritage of the last century. And in so doing, we are faced with more puzzles of history, of interpretation, of aesthetic evaluation than we are with perhaps any other major epoch of Western art. What, for instance, are we to do with the great whipping boys and girls of modern art history — Delaroche, Bouguereau, Rosa Bonheur — when we suddenly discover, with a blush of embarrassment or perverse pleasure, that some of their pictures are not thoroughly detestable? Should we reject, as methodical historians, a seductive anachronism like Gustave Doré's Romantic panorama of *The Scottish Highlands* (no. 32), because it was painted as late as 1875, one year after the First Impressionist Exhibition? How much attention should we now pay to admittedly minor masters like Jacque, Carolus-Duran, and Guillaumin, or provincial masters like Guigou and Ravier, when we are beguiled by their art but realize that it is historically dispensable, unmarked by the innovating fervor and restlessness of the great masters of the century? How can we make new kinds of order, new historical patterns out of the 19th-century's overwhelming abundance of art that is major and minor, true and meretricious, familiar and unfamiliar, personal and public? But at this stage of our swiftly changing attitudes toward the last century, firm answers to questions like these would be premature. What we need is much more evidence in the form of fresh juxtapositions of the heroes and the villains, the greater and the lesser artists of the period. The present exhibition in Minneapolis of a hundred-odd paintings from 19th-century France provides just such an occasion to help us look with different eyes at this surprisingly unknown historical domain.

One important way in which we can break through the traditionally hostile barriers that separate the 19th-century's progressive and conservative artists is by thinking of their work in terms of the kinds of subject or theme that often preoccupied both the most hidebound member of academic officialdom and the most Bohemian of anti-establishment rebels — a Delaroche and a Gauguin. One might consider, for example, how various 19th-century artists confronted the problem of religious painting, a problem particularly nagging in the century of Renan, Darwin, and Marx, and in the century when pictorial styles veered between extremes of abstraction and extremes of nearly photographic descriptive accuracy. How would traditional Christian martyrdoms be represented in this secularized period? Delaroche approaches the problem by viewing an innocent maiden of the age of Diocletian, martyred by drowning, as a Christian Ophelia in a Romantic, moonlit scene of murky mystery, where a halo alone must serve as the vehicle that would elevate this secular drama, painted with materialistic precision, to a supernatural realm (no. 29). Another painter, Théodule Ribot, attempted a contrary solution, one more consonant with the world of mid-19th-century Realism. His agonized *Saint Sebastian,* seen at the Salon of 1865 (no. 73), took its place with Manet's exactly contemporaneous efforts to translate Christian subject matter into modern experience by eliminating idealist components in favor of a brutal, immediate reality. As a critic of the Salon put it, "Ribot, finding his inspiration in the crude manner of Ribera, wantonly cultivates ugliness, but displays energetically pictorial qualities." But more often than not, this belief that Christian themes might be revitalized by the vigor of Spanish Baroque realism was abandoned. Later 19th-century masters like Jean-Jacques Henner tried to lend visual and spiritual credence to traditional Christian subjects by enveloping them, as in his *Mary Magdalene at the Tomb of the Saviour* of 1880 (no. 48), in a smoky pictorial ambiance which could slur over the collision of the real and the ideal that plagued so many 19th-century masters who essayed the great religious themes of Western art. Yet as the exhibition can demonstrate, these were not the only 19th-century solutions to this problem. More original was the introduction of a kind of spectator approach to Christianity, in which the artist observes piety almost as an outsider who longs to partake of it. Thus, Gauguin's *Yellow Christ* of 1889 (no. 37) is not a traditional painting of the *Crucifixion* in which the artist, by implication, shares a universal belief in the subject, but is rather a painting about simple Breton peasants whose faith is still so unchallenged by the religious doubts of the 19th-century that they can continue to worship innocently at the foot of a coarsely carved and painted yellow crucifix, a palpable symbol in actual Breton folk art of as yet unspoiled piety. Similarly, Maurice Denis' *Procession under the Trees* of 1892 (no. 30) is a painting that extols the beauty of Christian faith in a new way. We observe, almost as secular intruders, the silent procession of nuns walking through a convent garden, a movement so harmonious in its simple decorative patterns of filigreed blue shadow and white clerical silhouettes that its hushed and ordered serenity becomes the aesthetic equivalent of a religious experience. Such attitudes, if not such advanced pictorial styles, were to be found as well in more popular paintings of the century. Thus, a Romantic melodrama like Horace Vernet's *Italian Brigands Surprised by Papal Troops* of 1830 (no. 84) offers curious prophesies of this tourist view of simple Christianity. For here, a poignant note is struck by the piety of these Italian peasant women, attacked by brigands in front of a humble Christian shrine that is echoed on the other side of the road by a rude cross made of two branches. And in later 19th-century official paintings, we often find even more secularized interpretations of Christianity than these. In *Consolation* by Jean-Georges Vibert (no. 85), an artist who specialized in anecdotes of tender or humorous moments in the lives of the clergy, we glimpse a touching scene of Catholic confession, transposed from the church to a garden. Here, among a profusion of sunlit leaves and flowers that look as though they were painted by an artist who had never heard of Monet, a kind and elderly cleric takes time off from his gardening to offer spiritual consolation to a fashionable lady in a state of unnamed distress.

Like traditional concepts of religion, earlier attitudes toward rulers, warfare, and the dynamics of contemporary history were challenged in the 19th century. Already in the context of the Napoleonic epoch and its immediate aftermath, drastic changes can be observed in the recording of the great events of the day. When Parisian spectators at the Salon of 1804 saw Gros's enormous *Napoleon Visiting the Pesthouse at Jaffa* (represented in this exhibition by a smaller, more tightly painted version, no. 44), they had their faith in inherited concepts of history restored by this vision of Napoleon's almost supernatural powers and benevolence. Like a second coming of Christ, the leader of France enters a scene of the direst human misery to bring, with the miracle of his saintly touch, healing powers to the plague-stricken prisoners. But this propagandistic structure, in which a foreground of human suffering is ultimately justified by the nearly god-like goodness and power of the ruler is turned inside out in the following decades. Already in Géricault's *Raft of the Medusa* of 1819, seen here in a preparatory oil sketch (no. 40), the rational, omnipotent leader has disappeared. Instead, we are confronted with that new and typically 19th-century awareness of anonymous, mass humanity — in this case a shipload of human horror, far from salvation and almost as destitute of reason and guiding purpose as Géricault's *Mad Assassin* (no. 39), who plunges us still more intimately and frighteningly into the world of the irrational. And later, in works like Ferdinand Boissard de Boisdenier's bone-chilling glimpse of the retreat from Russia, a small sketch of the 1830s (no. 3), the Napoleonic myth is definitively destroyed. Here, the only realities left are the windswept gloom, the weary procession of faceless officers, the crow-filled, doom-ridden skies.

More and more, it was only the battles of past history — like that fought by St. Louis in 1242 and represented in Delacroix's sketch for the *Battle of Taillebourg* (no. 26) — which could still be conceived in terms of stunning pageantry, noble heroism, and ideal causes. Indeed, by the time we reach Meissonier's *Siege of Paris* (no. 56), an allegory of the heroic French resistance in the Franco-Prussian war of 1870-1871, we can no longer believe in the threadbare patriotic rhetoric of *La France,* who, with lion helmet, inspires this desperate defense, but look for relief instead in the truthful, almost photographic details of modern military costume. Other French painters working at the same time — Daumier, Degas, Monet, Caillebotte,

Sisley, Pissarro, Forain — recognized that modern history could no longer be represented in terms of such conventional allegories and that a prosaic view of a Parisian streetcorner, café, ballet class, industrial suburb, law court, or railway carriage could tell us far more about the realities of 19th-century life than these moribund heroics.

Equally precarious was the destiny of those 19th-century paintings that continued to illustrate the great imaginative themes culled from mythology and literature. What came so easily to painters who lived before the French Revolution — the creation of ideal figures who could convince us that they represented Venus, Apollo, Truth, Fame — was an ever more vexing problem to the masters who painted in a century that perpetually assaulted inherited ideals in favor of empirical truths. Thus, as in the case of religious paintings, these imaginative themes in 19th-century art exist in a tenuous pictorial world that demands, for success, high artistic powers. Prud'hon's *Union of Love and Friendship*, exhibited at the Salon of 1793 (no. 65), certainly can persuade us that its abstractions are vital: the ideal anatomies, the generalized chiaroscuro of Leonardo and Correggio still give credence to these strangely melancholy personifications. But other paintings, like Jean-Baptiste Regnault's *Toilet of Venus* (no. 70), may discomfit modern spectators in the peculiarly 19th-century collision of ideal forms and subjects with pictorial passages of photographic naturalism. That juxtaposition of the extremes of the abstract and the real reaches its most fascinating climax in the work of Ingres, whose *Roger and Angelica* (no. 50), a bizarre episode culled from Ariosto's *Orlando Furioso* that parallels such traditional maiden-dragon-hero themes as that of St. George or of Perseus, keeps shifting from totally imaginative reinventions of anatomy to quasi-photographic descriptions of feathers, rocks, armor, flesh.

It is not surprising that for us today, the most successful of these imaginative subject paintings are usually those that veil their legendary narratives in a smoky ambiance that avoids the 19th-century war between fact and fiction. Thus, Ary Scheffer's sketch for the ill-starred lovers, Paolo and Francesca, observed in rapt awe by Dante and Virgil (no. 76), is probably more appealing now than the finished Salon version of 1822, for the murky ether and slurring of detail permit us more easily to accept the visionary quality of the Dantesque subject. In the same way, two later masters of literary and mythological themes, Gustave Moreau and Odilon Redon, have achieved recognition even among devotees of progressive modern painting, thanks to the fact that they move farther and farther away from the photographic descriptiveness that can be so disturbing in the ideal subjects illustrated by the mid-century academicians. Thanks to its vibrant, jewel-like color and almost hallucinatory landscape background, Moreau's *Hercules and the Hydra* of 1867 (no. 62), can make us believe again in the world of Greek heroes and monsters; and by the time we reach Redon's *Apollo,* painted after the turn of the century (no. 69), this Huysmans-like vision of a precious, remote world has become so imprecise, so narcotically dream-like, that we can barely discern the classical subject of Apollo driving his chariot and almost find ourselves in that 20th-century world of chromatic abstraction heralded in Sérusier's *Talisman* (no. 77). Yet if such literary and mythological themes seem almost literally to vanish in Redon's work, they are often subject to surprising reappearances in the work of painters more securely rooted in a realist tradition. It is not only a question of so astute an observer of the Parisian commonplace as Degas venturing, in the 1860s, into a Biblical subject like the *Daughter of Jephthah* (no. 25) and producing a work whose mannerist spaces and diffuse actions pinpoint the sudden horror of the father who unwittingly condemns his own daughter to death, but it is also a matter of how subjects that are in no way explicitly imaginative can become so through the force of earlier Western traditions. Thus, Renoir's *Bathers* of 1897 (no.71) is so saturated with the ideal robustness and vitality of Venetian and Rubensian traditions that, were the painting to be called the *Nymphs of Diana,* we could easily accept that identification. Similarly, Henri-Edmond Cross's *Excursion (La Ronde)* of 1895 (no. 20) presents so serene and so generalized a vision of man and the bounty of landscape that we might almost accept it as a modern interpretation of that academic image of classical Arcadia perpetuated more literally in the work of such 19th-century official painters as Puvis de Chavannes.

No less than classical themes, exotic ones permeated both official and avant-garde 19th-century painting in many strange guises that run the gamut from documentary, touristic curiosity to Romantic reveries upon a total escape from the grim, unexotic facts of industrialized Paris. The

Napoleonic campaigns permitted, in journalistic terms, the intrusion of such Near Eastern data as the architecture and costume that provide picturesque relief to the horrors of Gros's *Pesthouse at Jaffa* (no. 44); and soon, in the work of Delacroix, this exploration of a non-Western world could take up the entire pictorial stage. Thus, in the *Fanatics of Tangier* (no. 27), we are thrust into a spectacle of Arab religious frenzy — the convulsive gyrations of the Yssaouïs sect after prayer — which sweeps us away from the dreary, workaday realities of the modern city to a world where human passions are as uninhibited as the blaze of North African light and color. Voluptuous extremes could also be found in the Orient, witness Delacroix's *Turkish Woman Bathing* (no. 28), an exotic Garden of Eden where robust, sensual women are happily innocent of the restrictions imposed by mid-19th-century society.

Just how tantalizingly remote from Parisian life these exotic worlds must have appeared is nowhere seen more entertainingly than in Gérôme's official illustration of the meeting of Imperial East and West, (no. 41), exhibited at the Salon of 1865 to a popular audience whose descendants, a century later, would flock to see *The King and I*. In the *grand salon* of the Palace of Fontainebleau, the Emperor and Empress of France are seen receiving the ambassadors sent to Paris by the Emperor of Siam (Chao-Pha-Mongkout, Lord of the White Elephants), who, in the 1850s, tried successfully to establish active trade between Bangkok and Europe. Here, the pompous portrait gallery of Second Empire worthies (including Mérimée in the center and, on the left, a group of official painters, Meissonier, Jadin, and Gérôme himself) fades into the prosaic in the face of the extravagant servility of the Siamese envoys and the strange array of exotic crown, throne, and parasols that arrest our attention in the foreground. When, nearly three decades later in Tahiti, Gauguin painted *Under the Pandanus* (no. 36), he may well have scorned the glossy, mirror-like truth of Gérome's virtuoso naturalism, but he nevertheless perpetuated, in its most extreme form, Gérome's and all of Paris' fascination for the beauties of non-Western peoples and art, for the simple felicities of a civilization as yet uncorrupted by the evils of the Industrial Revolution.

For those less passionate and adventurous than Delacroix and Gauguin, the landscape of France itself could usually provide a more prosaic and accessible equivalent of non-Western exoticism. Indeed, the overwhelming abundance in 19th-century Paris of paintings that represented the unspoiled landscape and the unspoiled peasants of rural France speaks for the growing appeal that a simple vision of hills and valleys, lakes and rivers, sunrises and sunsets, sheep and shepherds must have had as a vicarious relief to the stresses and complexities of urban life. Often, specific sites are recorded with the eye of an escapist who seeks the remedies of nature. Thus, Diaz de la Peña can take us to a cloistered clearing in the forest of Fontainebleau (no. 31); Harpignies can show us the shimmering effect of a moonrise on the Loire (no. 47); Paul Flandrin can transform the shores of the Gardon into an Arcadian idyl of classical timelessness (no. 34); Guigou can exhilarate our senses with an expansive vista of the rugged, sun-drenched foothills of Provence (no. 45) that would later inspire Van Gogh (no. 42). And often, these natural environments are inhabited by figures who seem to have come to them intentionally to enjoy the pleasures of meditation and tranquility. Corot's mysterious, nymph-like *Liseuse* (no. 16) is one of these, as are her many prosaic descendants in later 19th-century painting: the well-dressed couple on a leisurely outing in Carolus-Duran's *Promenade in the Woods* (no. 8); *Mlle. Pontillon*, the sister of Berthe Morisot, caught by this lady impressionist in a mood of elegant solitude (no. 63), a sophisticated urbanite enjoying the relaxation of the country; or the daughters of the Parisian dealer Durand-Ruel, who, as painted by Renoir in 1882 (no. 72), are similarly immersed in the rejuvenating pleasures of sunlit flowers and trees.

The tonic powers of nature for the Parisian spectator were apparent, too, in the many pictures of peasants and domesticated animals, most often viewed through idealist lenses. Rosa Bonheur's internationally famous *Horse Fair,* first seen at the Salon of 1853 and later inspected personally by Queen Victoria at Buckingham Palace, is such a work (no. 4). It translates the commonplace pageantry of the Parisian horse market on the Boulevard de l'Hôpital into a language that smacks not only of the impassioned, Romantic fury of Géricault's and Vernet's horses, but even of such classical prototypes as the Quirinale *Horsetamers.* These ennobled visions of simple animals and people reach further extremes in later 19th-century paintings like that by Charles Jacque of 1880, in which a rugged shepherd, alone with his flock, is invested with a brooding drama of almost Biblical grandeur (no. 52); or by Bouguereau of 1878, in which a peasant mother and child on a donkey are so idealized by allusions to old-master paintings of classical and Christian subjects that the work might almost be called the *Triumph of the Infant Bacchus* or the *Flight into Egypt* rather than the *Return from the Harvest* (no. 6); or, more light-heartedly, by Bastien-Lepage, whose *Pas Mèche (Nothing Doing)* of 1882 (no. 1) views a farm boy as picturesquely tattered and charmingly puckish rather than as the victim of those appalling conditions of child labor, in city and country, that would preoccupy so many 19th-century social reformers and even artists.

Within this realm of bucolic sentiment and fantasy, no harsher note could be struck than that of Courbet, whose *Siesta* of 1868 (no. 18), with its graceless array of clumsily somnolent farmers and cattle, suddenly dispels the idealist haze that clung to so many 19th-century popular paintings of rural life. And in an urban context too, this intrusion of the real, of the literally unvarnished truth becomes more and more conspicuous in works of the second half of the century. One need only compare early 19th-century views of the city of Rouen with Pissarro's 1896 view of the same city (no. 64) to realize that something drastic has happened to both French art and French life — Romantic panoramas, animated by peasants and dramatically punctuated by the silhouettes of Gothic cathedral towers, give way to a contracted view of a bustling industrial city on a rainy workday, animated by streetcars, carriages, and umbrella-carrying pedestrians, and crowned by a factory's puffing smokestack.

Indeed, it is within this expanding world of the city that some of the most startling innovations of 19th-century French painting occur, changes that finally come to pictorial grips with that new urban sense of vast and anonymous flux, of multiple and diverse activities. Monet's *Gare St. Lazare* series of 1877 (no. 60) is one of the most famous enquiries into this new experience, pictures whose stenographic brushstrokes can seize the spectacle of a modern railroad station where all is volatile: clouds of steam from the engines, crowds of rushing passengers, shimmers of light dissolving the glass-and-iron roof of the train shed. Yet even in a drier, more literal style, the same kind of urban sensations can be caught, sensations so unlike the focused narrative of communal experiences recorded earlier in the century in Boilly's vignettes of Parisian life (no. 2). Thus, Caillebotte's unforgettable *Place de l'Europe on a Rainy Day* of 1877 (no. 7) suddenly discloses those facts of the modern city which we still know firsthand a century later. Here nameless pedestrians, alone and in pairs, walk up, down, and across the great traffic arteries of Paris, creating a startlingly random nexus of movement that pinpoints the prosaic truth of the city's constant pulse. The same centrifugal rhythms of private lives and private thoughts can be seen in Degas' *Ballet Class* (no. 23), where the anonymous chaperon, absorbed in the daily newspaper, keeps distracting our attention from the painting's nominal subject, the lessons of a ballet class. Even in portraiture, this fresh awareness of simultaneous, even contradictory experiences can be observed. Unlike such earlier 19th-century portraits as those by David, Gérard, or Ingres (no. 51), where our attention is fully concentrated on the revelation of a single sitter, that by Degas of the artist's father, Auguste, and the Spanish tenor and guitarist, Pagans, sets up a curious, see-sawing rivalry which forces us to shift restlessly from one personality to the other, from the performing musician to the passive listener, from the young man to the old one, with neither sitter ever gaining decisively the larger part of our sympathy or attention (no. 24).

By the end of the century, however, many French artists retreated from this investigation of the facts of modern life into a world of personal aesthetic order that moved farther and farther away from an observation of the commonplace. Seurat's 1888 series of paintings of the Norman fishing town, Port-en-Bessin (no. 78), provides several cases in point: in Minneapolis' own painting of this port, the somewhat gritty, uncompromising facts of the footbridge, the jetties, the ugly houses, the isolated figures (a customs officer, a working woman, and a child) are all literal enough to locate the painting in the earlier French tradition of recording specific ports, as Corot's of La Rochelle (no. 17). But in the Museum of Modern Art's view of the same harbor (no. 79), such topographical and sociological detail is suppressed almost beyond recognition in a highly refined mosaic pattern of receding ellipses accented by the bobbing diminuendo rhythms of distant white sails. Cézanne, too, moved away from the literalness of an earlier 19th-century generation. Unlike the still lifes of Fantin-Latour or Manet (nos. 33, 55), which evoke a particular moment of enjoyment and hospitality in an elegant French home, his arrangement of a vase, fruit, and cloth upon a table transcends commonplace domestic use and becomes a world of wholly private contemplation (no. 13). Similarly, Cézanne's interpretation of the Jas du Bouffan (no. 12), for all its fidelity to the rows of paired chestnut trees on his father's property near Aix and for all its dependence upon earlier French landscape formulas of vistas seen through a screen of trees, nevertheless moves into a realm of intensely personal order, a unique construction whose ambiguous shuffling of near and far positions in illusory depth depends on the artist's sensibility alone and on no inherited public traditions of spatial organization. Monet, too, in his *Poplars* of 1891 (no. 61) enters a strange, subjective world where the communal urban bustle of his *Gare St. Lazare* series of 1877 is replaced by a hazy reverie so subjective and so dreamlike that it almost inhabits the same fantastic ether as Redon's *Apollo* (no. 69).

And in other works of the *fin-de-siècle,* this aestheticized realm, in which a motif in nature can at times be transformed almost beyond recognition, is even more explicit. Thus, Georges Lacombe, in *The Yellow Sea (Camaret)* of 1892 (no. 53), takes a theme common enough in mid-19th-century landscape painting — the rugged portions of the Norman and Breton coastlines that had provided a savage background to works like Paul Huet's *Cliffs at Houlgate* (no. 49), a shipwreck melodrama at the Salon of 1863 — but translates it into a flat tempera pattern of almost Japanese artifice, in which the silhouettes of bizarre geological formations are played off against the linear calligraphy of waves. Similarly, Eugène Carrière's *Maternity,* also of the 1890s (no. 10), retains a familiar and often academic 19th-century subject (the ineffable tenderness of mother love), but renders it newly evocative and mysterious by enveloping the figures in a monochrome fog that threatens to vaporize them entirely. In the 1890s, Vuillard, too, turns the domestic into the magical, as in the *Interior at L'Etang-la-Ville* of 1893 (no. 86), where three occupants of a room are almost dissolved in the hushed and vibrant twinkling of a multitude of cloth and wallpaper patterns. And, most famous of these straws in an abstract wind, there is Paul Sérusier's tiny Brittany landscape, painted on a cigar-box lid at Pont-Aven in October, 1888, under Gauguin's tutelage and brought back to Paris as a kind of pictorial talisman that could and did astonish a new generation of painters (no. 77). Here, the older master persuaded his young disciple to push his colors to a point of such paint-tube purity — yellow, green, vermillion, ultramarine — that they almost camouflage completely the common motif of secluded trees, leaves, water, and cottage so beloved by earlier 19th-century landscape painters. Indeed, with pictures like these, where contours, atmosphere, pattern, hue suddenly lead lives of their own, we are almost through the looking-glass of 19th-century French painting and stand at that precarious brink in modern art where abstract means and realist ends have finally been rent asunder.

ROBERT ROSENBLUM
Professor of Fine Arts
New York University

CATALOGUE
OF THE
EXHIBITION

All dimensions are given in inches. In each case height precedes width.

JULES BASTIEN-LEPAGE

Damvillers, 1848-1884, Paris

Despite parental opposition to his painting, an early stint as a French civil servant, and the disastrous war of 1870, Bastien-Lepage launched his artistic career with the Salon of 1873. Training had come through the Ecole des Beaux-Arts and a brief sojourn at the atelier of Cabanel. Success was not immediate, however, and the Salon of 1874 saw him adopt a rustic subject matter which was later to become his forte. Realistic in outlook, his mature style was based largely on Courbet and the early Manet. The peasants of the Meuse became his major preoccupation and, with a sentiment akin to that of Millet, he continued to romanticize their life and land until his untimely death in 1884.

1. PAS MÈCHE, 1882

(Nothing Doing)
Oil on canvas, 52 x 35
Signed and dated, lower left: J. Bastien-Lepage/Damvillers/82.
National Gallery of Scotland, Edinburgh

EX-COLL: A. Tooth, London, February 28, 1885; H. J. Turner, 1902; George M'Culloch, May 23, 1913; Wallis & Sons, London.

EXHIBITIONS: *Bastien-Lepage Memorial Exhibition*, Paris (1885), *Exhibition*, Glasgow (1888), No. 675; *Exposition centennale de l'art français*, Paris (1900), No. 89; *Nineteenth Century French Paintings*, Bournemouth, Russell-Cotes Art Gallery (1960).

LITERATURE: W. E. Henley, *A Century of Artists* (1889).

JEAN-FREDERIC BAZILLE

Montpellier, 1841-1870, Montpellier

A pioneer of Impressionism who died too young to leave a large body of work, Bazille first studied in Gleyre's studio with fellow students Monet and Renoir with whom he frequently made holiday excursions to the forest of Fontainebleau and the seashore. Bazille's student days were divided between painting and medical studies. The latter he pursued to satisfy his parents, who in turn gave him a steady allowance sufficiently large for him to also offer Monet thirty francs a month. Bazille's preoccupation with charm and solidity differed greatly from the experimental, fugitive effects sought by the other Impressionists. He joined the Zouaves during the Franco-Prussian War and was killed at the age of 29.

1a. PAYSAGE AU BORD DU LEZ, 1870

(Landscape by the River Lez)
Oil on canvas, 54½ x 79½
Signed and dated, lower left: F. Bazille 1870
The Minneapolis Institute of Arts

EX-COLL: Marc Bazille (brother of artist); Frédéric Bazille (grandson of artist); Mme. Guerschmain, Paris; Walter P. Chrysler, Jr., New York.

EXHIBITIONS: *Bazille,* Montpellier, Musée Fabre (1927), No. 31; *Centenaire de Bazille,* Montpellier, Musée Fabre (1941), No. 38; *Bazille,* Paris, Wildenstein and Co. (1950), No. 66.

LITERATURE: G. Poulain, *Bazille et ses amis* (Paris, 1932), p. 181, 202; F. Daulte, *Frédéric Bazille et son temps* (Geneva, 1955), No. 55, p. 113, 189, ill.

LOUIS-LEOPOLD BOILLY

La Bassée, 1761-1845, Paris

One of the most prolific artists of the century, Boilly is estimated to have produced more than 5,000 portraits and 500 genre scenes in his lifetime. A meticulous worker, he began his career in La Bassée under the tutelage of his father and must at some point have been influenced by the clarity and detail of Dutch painting. By 1779 at the age of eighteen years he was installed in Arras in which town alone he completed 300 portraits. In 1784 he went to Paris, and from 1791 he exhibited works in the Salons, generally contributing popular *scènes galantes* which were widely engraved. From 1793 his paintings were more in keeping with the aims and tastes of the Revolution, and his numerous depictions of scenes and modes of the time earned him the title of "historian of the Revolution."

2. DISTRIBUTION DE VINS ET DE COMESTIBLES AUX CHAMPS-ELYSÉES POUR LA FÊTE DU ROI, 1822

(Distribution of Wine and Food on the Champs-Elysées for the King's Festival)
Oil on canvas, 38⅛ x 50¾
Signed and dated, lower right: Boilly, 1822
Musée Carnavalet, Paris

EX-COLL: Boilly Sale, Paris, January 3, 1829, No. 1; M. Duval (1865); Demere (1902); Le musée du Petit-Palais; Musée Carnavalet (1934).

EXHIBITIONS: *Salon*, Paris (1822), No. 120; *Boilly*, Paris, Salle Lebrun, No. 13; *Exposition centennale de l'exposition universelle*, Paris, (1900), No. 41; *Exposition Boilly*, Paris, Musée de l'Orangerie (1930), No. 10; *De Poussin à Ingres*, Hamburg and Munich (1952); *The Taste of Paris*, Atlanta (1968), No. 38, ill.

LITERATURE: H. Harrisse, *L. L. Boilly* (Paris, 1898), No. 45, pp. 84, 99, 166; *Le peintre L. L. Boilly* (Paris, 1913), pp. 119, 120, 152, 273, ill. pl. XLV; Ch. Mabille de Poncheville, *L. L. Boilly* (Paris, 1931), pp. 129, 131, 132, ill. p. 128.

159.4   171666p

c.1

JOSEPH-FERDINAND BOISSARD DE BOISDENIER

Château Roux, 1813-1866, Paris

Almost forgotten today, Boissard was a representative of those second-generation Romantic painters whose main interests were detailed interiors, historical and moralizing subjects, and portraits. He was a pupil of Gros and Deveria. At the Salon of 1835 he exhibited his most famous work, *An Episode in the Retreat from Moscow* (now at Rouen). He was a friend of Daumier and Baudelaire. Boissard was an eccentric artistic personality, but when he is at his finest, his work recalls the intensity of Gros and Géricault.

3. RETREAT FROM MOSCOW

Oil on canvas, 6¼ x 10½

Signed, lower right: Boissard de Boisdenier
Lent by Mr. and Mrs. Germain Seligman, New York

EX-COLL: P. M. Adda, Liverpool, England.

EXHIBITIONS: *Delacroix, ses maîtres, ses amis, ses élèves*, Bordeaux (1963), No. 212.

LITERATURE: René Huyghe, *L'art et l'âme* (Paris, n.d.), p. 438, ill.

MARIE-ROSALIE BONHEUR

Bordeaux, 1822-1899, Melun

Rosa Bonheur, daughter of the painter Raymond Bonheur, was the eldest of four children, all of whom became artists. While studying under her father in Paris, she exhibited considerable drawing ability and in 1841 made her debut at the Salon at the age of nineteen. During her long and prolific painting career she received hundreds of prizes and was the first woman ever to receive the Grand Cross of the Legion of Honor.

She exhibited paintings, and occasionally sculpture, at the Salon regularly, and it was her *Horse Fair* at the Salon of 1853 which put her in the first rank of contemporary painters. A close friendship with Queen Victoria made her works especially popular in England. Rosa Bonheur's specialty was animal paintings, and it is for these realistic and skillful portrayals that she is chiefly remembered.

4. HORSE FAIR, 1853

Oil on canvas, 96¼ x 199½
Signed and dated, lower left: Rosa Bonheur 1853
The Metropolitan Museum of Art, New York
Gift of Cornelius Vanderbilt (87.25)

EX-COLL: Ernest Gambart, London, 1855-1857; William P. Wright, New Jersey, 1857-1877; A. T. Stewart, New York, 1877; Cornelius Vanderbilt, New York.

EXHIBITIONS: *Salon,* Paris (1853), No. 134; *Exposition nationale et triennale (Salon of 1853),* Ghent, Palais d l'Université, No. 29; *Cinquième exposition,* Bordeaux, Galerie de la Société des Amis des Arts (1854) No. 78; *Second Annual Exhibition of the French School of Fine Arts,* Pall Mall, London, French Gallery (1855), No. 24; *First Exhibition of the French School of Fine Arts,* London (1856), Birmingham (1856), Manchester, Royal Institution (1856), No. 27.

LITERATURE: L. Clément de Ris, *L'Artiste* (1853), series 5, X, pp. 148ff; F. Henriet, *Coup d'oeil sur le Salon de 1853* (1853), p. 18; E. de Mirecourt, *Rosa Bonheur* (1856), pp. 85ff; L. Rogers-Miles, *Rosa Bonheur* (1900), pp. 50-60, 62-65, 170, 180, 182, ill. pp. 43, 57; Metropolitan Museum of Art, *Catalogue of Paintings* (New York, 1900), pp. 194ff, No. 654; F. Hird, *Rosa Bonheur* (1904), pp. 70-77, ill. opp. p. 70; A. Klumpke, *Rosa Bonheur* (1908), pp. 1ff, 221-231, 424, 430-434, ill. opp. p. 226.

EUGENE BOUDIN

Honfleur, 1824-1898, Paris

One of the precursors of Impressionism, Boudin was primarily a painter of subjects pertaining to the sea and is best known for his beachscapes and scenes of harbour life. He was a student of Isabey. He first exhibited in the Salon of 1859, and his talent was recognized at that time by Baudelaire. He was a friend of Monet and was an influential artist for many of the young Impressionists, participating in the first Impressionist Exhibition of 1874.

5. LES LAVEUSES AU BORD DE LA TOUQUES A TROUVILLE, ca. 1890

(Washerwomen)
Oil on canvas, 16 x 21⅞
Signed, lower right: E. Boudin
Lent by Miss Alice Tully, New York

EX-COLL: Boussod-Valadon; Schmit.

EXHIBITIONS: *Eugène Boudin,* Paris, Galerie Schmit (1965), No. 88; *Eugène Boudin,* New York, Hirschl and Adler (1966), No. 43, ill. in color.

LITERATURE: *Art in America* (September, 1965); *Pictures on Exhibit* (1965).

ADOLPHE-WILLIAM BOUGUEREAU

La Rochelle, 1825-1905, La Rochelle

Having lived and worked as an important artist during the greater part of a century of change and artistic innovation, Bouguereau has perhaps fallen further from a once esteemed position than any other of his contemporaries. He is thought of as a diehard conservative associated with the reactionary French Academy, barring every new development. At the height of his career and power, he heaped derision upon those he considered contemptible — the Impressionists. His competent drawing, meticulous execution, even color, and flat surface texture were the hallmarks of his "fine technique," for which he was highly regarded. His frank presentation of the idealized nude figure seemed to add importance and seriousness to his work. He pleased the public and was one of the most decorated of French 19th-century artists. His work has not suited the contemporary preference for more spontaneity and innovation, but from a historical point of view it cannot be ignored or forgotten. It represents the durable and lingering academic tradition which often seems to be the ground upon which new art can be built.

6. RETURN FROM THE HARVEST, 1878

Oil on canvas, 94 x 64
Signed and dated, lower left: W. Bouguereau 1878
Cummer Gallery of Art, Jacksonville

EX-COLL: B. F. Albee; Hirschl & Adler Galleries.

EXHIBITIONS: *Salon and Independent Artists of the 1880s,* Pomona, California, Pomona College (April 16-May 12, 1963); *Artists of the Paris Salon,* Jacksonville, Cummer Gallery of Art (January 7-February 2, 1964).

GUSTAVE CAILLEBOTTE

Paris, 1848-1894, Gennevilliers

As a man perhaps best known for his superb bequest of Impressionist paintings to the French government, Caillebotte has only recently become known to the general public as a talented painter. A wealthy and active champion of Impressionism, Caillebotte helped to organize many of its early exhibitions while at the same time giving financial aid and support to his artist friends. As a painter himself, Caillebotte trained at the Beaux-Arts, quickly passing from a naturalistic to a quasi-impressionist manner of working indebted to Degas. His views of Parisian scenes utilize plunging perspectives, drastic foreshortenings, and patterned effects which anticipate the later work of Pissarro as well as certain aspects of 20th-century Surrealism. "Art patron, painter, lover of literature, yachtsman, and gardener," Caillebotte was, in the words of Denys Sutton, "the type of man for whom the modern world no longer seems to hold a place."

7. PLACE DE L'EUROPE ON A RAINY DAY, 1877

(Umbrellas in the Place de l'Europe)
Oil on canvas, 83½ x 108¾
Signed and dated, lower left: G. Caillebotte, 1877
The Art Institute of Chicago, Chicago
Charles H. and Mary F. S. Worcester Fund Income

EX-COLL: Collection of the artist (1877-1894); Martial Caillebotte, Paris (1894-1900); Georges Minoret, Château de Montglat, Provins (1900-1950); M. Chardeau, Paris (1950-1954); Walter P. Chrysler, Jr., New York.

EXHIBITIONS: *Catalogue de la IIIe exposition de peinture,* Paris, 6 rue Le Peletier, (April, 1877); *Exposition retrospective d'oeuvres de G. Caillebotte,* Paris, Galerie Durand-Ruel (June, 1894), No. 47, p. 5; *Caillebotte,* Paris, Wildenstein (1915), No. 13; *Paintings from the collection of Walter P. Chrysler, Jr.,* Portland, Art Museum (1956), No. 78, p. 47.

LITERATURE: Georges Rivière, "L'impressionniste," *Journal d'art* (April 14, 1877); Lionello Venturi, *Les archives de l'impressionnisme* (Paris and New York, 1939); Marie Bérhaut, *Gustave Caillebotte* (Paris, 1951), No. 28; Fernand Hazan, ed., *Dictionnaire de la peinture moderne* (Paris, 1954), p. 43; John Maxon, "Some Recent Acquisitions," *Apollo* (September, 1966), Vol. LXXXIV, pp. 171, 216 (detail in color on cover).

CHARLES-EMILE-AUGUSTE DURAND
(CAROLUS-DURAN)

Lille, 1838-1917, Paris

Carolus-Duran, painter of portraits, landscapes, and genre pictures, began his studies at the Lille Academy, and later studied in Paris, Italy, and Spain. He became familiar with and drew from the work of Velasquez. He perhaps is best known as a portrait painter although his influence as head of one of the principal ateliers in Paris is widely recognized. In 1889 he was made Commander of the Legion of Honor and in 1904 he became a member of the Académie des Beaux-Arts. A year later, he was appointed Director of the French Academy at Rome, succeeding Guillaume.

8. LA PROMENADE SOUS BOIS, 1861

(Promenade in the Woods)
Oil on canvas, 56¼ x 99¾
Signed and dated, lower right
Lent by Mr. Walter P. Chrysler, Jr., New York

EX-COLL: Acquired from the artist's son.

EXHIBITIONS: *French Paintings 1789-1929 from the Collection of Walter P. Chrysler, Jr.,* Dayton, Ohio, The Dayton Art Institute (March 25-May 22, 1960), No. 39.

LITERATURE: The Dayton Art Institute, *French Paintings 1789-1929 from the Collection of Walter P. Chrysler, Jr.,* No. 39, p. 131.

JEAN-BAPTISTE CARPEAUX
Valenciennes, 1827-1875, Courbevoie

In a century which produced a veritable marble forest of pretentious Neo-Classic sculpture, the names of Rude, Carpeaux, and Rodin stand out. Carpeaux was both a painter and sculptor and was Rude's most eminent pupil. His best work reflects the French sensibility seen in 18th-century painting by artists such at Watteau, Boucher, and Fragonard. He resisted the pseudo-classical and in *Dancing*, his well-known sculptural group at the Paris Opera, he captured a kind of Bacchic gusto differing from the tendencies of the times. In his paintings as in his sculpture, the figures in many groups are full of gratuitous movement entangled amid contrasting light and shadows. He softened the Baroque elements of his master Rude, and together they provided an alternative to the academic style which was to be the point of departure for Rodin later in the century.

9. LE PRINCE IMPÉRIAL DISTRIBUTANT LES RÉCOMPENSES
À L'EXPOSITION DE 1867

(The distribution of Awards)
Oil on canvas, 15 x 18⅛
Signed, lower right: Bte CARPEAUX
Musée Classé des Beaux-Arts, Valenciennes

EX-COLL: Mme J. Bte Carpeaux, Carpeaux Sale (December 8-9, 1913), No. 118; Fabiux.

EXHIBITIONS: *Carpeaux*, Paris, Ecole nationale des Beaux-Arts (May, 1894), No. 83; *Carpeaux*, Brussels, À la toison d'or (1896), No. 30; *Carpeaux*, Paris, Petit-Palais (1955-1956), No. 145; *Carpeaux*, Nice, Musée des Ponchettes (1956), No. 91.

LITERATURE: Louise Clement, *La vérité sur l'oeuvre et la vie de Jean-Baptiste Carpeaux* (Paris, 1934), I, p. 208.

EUGENE CARRIERE

Gournay, 1849-1906, Paris

Beginning in a traditional fashion at the Ecole des Beaux-Arts and the studio of Cabanel, Carrière later developed into one of the most individualistic and original of all 19th-century artists and, in his prime, was one of the most widely known and respected of French artists. The hallmarks of his style are a pervading mixture of melancholy, sentimentality, and tenderness set in an evanescent, misty atmosphere. This latter trait caused Degas to quip, "They've been smoking again in the children's room."

10. MATERNITÉ, ca. 1892

(Maternity)
Oil on canvas, 37¾ x 45¾
Museum of Modern Art, New York
Anonymous Gift, 1942

EX-COLL: Adolph Lewisohn; Sam A. Lewisohn.

EXHIBITIONS: Eugène Carrière, Allentown, Art Museum (November 2, 1968-January 31, 1969).

LITERATURE: Stephan Bourgeois, E. Weyhe, *The Adolph Lewisohn Collection of Modern French Paintings and Sculptures* (New York, 1968), ill. opp. p. 114.

PAUL CEZANNE

Aix-en-Provence, 1839-1906, Aix-en-Provence

After initial studies in Aix-en-Provence where he first met Émile Zola, Cézanne went to Paris in 1861. He there encountered Pissarro and Guillaumin and later Manet and the artists of the café Guerbois group. First drawn to Impressionism, he met with disappointment at the official Salons and withdrew himself to his family's property at Jas du Bouffan in Provence, away from what he called the "Bouguereau Salon." Cézanne developed a more and more personal style combining the past (Poussin) with the present (Pissarro) and ultimately evolved an approach to art which laid the foundations for Cubism. He saw nature as composed of variations of the cube, the sphere and the triangle and in so doing became one of the most influential artists of the 19th century.

11. PORTRAIT D'AMBROISE VOLLARD

(The Dealer, Ambroise Vollard)
Oil on canvas, 39⅜ x 32¼
Musée du Petit Palais, Paris

EX-COLL: Bequeathed to the museum by Vollard, 1945.

EXHIBITIONS: *Cézanne*, Paris, Musée de l'Orangerie (1936), No. 101, pl. 8; *Quelques oeuvres des collections de la Ville de Paris*, Bern, La Chaux-de-Fonds, Geneva, Basel (1947), No. 17; *Exhibition*, Petit Palais, Musée de la Ville de Paris, Zurich, Kunsthaus (1947), No. 180; *Biennale Internationale*, Venice (1948), No. 463; *Franse meesters uit het Petit Palais*, Rotterdam, Museum Boymans (1952-53), No. 15; *Capolavori della pittura francese dell'ottocento*, Rome, Palazzo delle Esposizioni (1955), ill. No. 89; *Les Sources du XXe siècle*, Paris, Musée national d'art moderne (1960-61), No. 85; *The Taste of Paris*, Atlanta, The High Museum of Art (1968), ill.

LITERATURE: A. Vollard, *Cézanne* (1914), pp. 91-107, ill. pl. 51; T. Klingsor, *Cézanne* (Paris, 1926), p. 44, ill. p. 42; G. Mack, *Paul Cézanne* (London), pp. 346-348, ill. pl. 38; L. Venturi, *Cézanne — son art, son oeuvre* (Paris, 1936), Vol. I, p. 214, No. 696, ill.; J. Rewald, *Paul Cézanne, correspondence* (Paris, 1937), p. 237, letter 140; J. Rewald, *Paul Cézanne: A Biography* (New York, 1949), ill. pl. 92, cit. pp. 170 and 220; F. Novotny, *Cézanne* (Phaidon, 1948), ill. pl. 75, cit. p. 14; C. Pissarro, *Lettres à son fils Lucien* (Paris, 1950), p. 432; A. Vollard, *Souvenirs d'un marchand de tableaux* (Paris, 1957), ill. p. 170; A. Martini and R. Negri, *Cézanne e il post impressionismo* (Milan, 1967), ill. p. 37, pl. II.

PAUL CEZANNE

Aix-en-Provence, 1839-1906, Aix-en-Provence

12. MARRONNIERS AU JAS DE BOUFFAN

(Chestnut Trees at Jas du Bouffan)
Oil on canvas, 27¾ x 35¼
The Minneapolis Institute of Arts, Minneapolis
William Hood Dunwoody Fund (49.9)

EX-COLL: Egisto Fabbri, Florence; Paul Rosenberg and Company, New York and Paris; Wildenstein Galleries, New York; Georges Wildenstein, Paris; The Frick Collection, New York.

EXHIBITIONS: *Exposition Cézanne,* Paris, Bernheim-Jeune (January 10-22, 1910), No. 21; *Esposizione Internazionale d'Arte della Citta di Venezia: Mostra Individuale di Paul Cézanne,* Venice (1920), No. 10, ill.; *First Loan Exposition of the Museum of Modern Art,* New York (November, 1929), No. 19, ill.; *Important Paintings from the Collections of Leading New York Dealers,* New York, American Art Association, Anderson Galleries (March 15-April 4, 1931), No. 113; *Nineteenth-Century Masterpieces,* London, Wildenstein (1935), No. 7; *Diamond Jubilee,* Philadelphia, Museum of Art (November 4-February 11, 1950-51), No. 85; *Cézanne,* Chicago, Art Institute (February 7-March 16, 1952), p. 58; *Cézanne,* New York, The Metropolitan Museum of Art, (April 4-May 16, 1952); *Twentieth Anniversary Exhibition,* Kansas City, William Rockhill Nelson Gallery of Art (December 11-31, 1953); *Exhibition,* Edinburgh, Royal Scottish Academy (August 20-September 18, 1954), No. 36; *Exhibition,* London, Tate Gallery (September 28-October 27, 1954).

LITERATURE: L. Venturi, *Cézanne — son art, son oeuvre* (Paris, 1936), No. 476, p. 167, ill.; Novotny, *Cézanne und das ende der Wissenschaftlichen Perspective* (Vienna, 1938), No. 54, p. 200, B. Dorival, *Cézanne* (Boston, 1950), pl. 69; *The Minneapolis Institute of Arts Bulletin* (December 31, 1948), Vol. XXXVII pp. 197-198; *The Minneapolis Istitute of Arts Bulletin* (January 7, 1950), Vol. XXXIX, pp. 1-7; M. Shapiro, *Paul Cézanne* (New York, 1952), pp. 72-73; *Art News* (April, 1952), pp. 28-33; *The Minneapolis Institute of Arts Bulletin* (January, 1955), Vol. XLV, p. 5.

PAUL CÉZANNE

Aix-en-Provence, 1839-1906, Aix-en-Provence

13. RIDEAU, CRUCHON, ET COMPOTIER, ca. 1893-1894

(Still Life)
Oil on canvas, 23¼ x 28½
Lent by Mr. and Mrs. John Hay Whitney, New York

EX-COLL: Ambroise Vollard, Paris; C. Hoogendijk, The Hague (acquired before 1914); Paul Rosenberg, Paris; Durand-Ruel, Paris-New York; Dr. Albert C. Barnes, Barnes Foundation, Merion, Pennsylvania (acquired 1922-1923); New York art market.

EXHIBITIONS: *New York Collectors,* New York, Museum of Modern Art (1951); *Cézanne,* Chicago, Art Institute, and New York, The Metropolitan Museum of Art (1952), No. 82; *Cinquantenaire de la mort de Cézanne,* Aix-en-Provence, Pavillon de Vendôme (July-August, 1956), No. 50; *Paul Cézanne,* Munich, Haus der Kunst (October-November 1956), No. 53; *Cézanne,* London, Tate Gallery (December, 1960-January 1961).

LITERATURE: A. C. Barnes, *The Art in Painting* (New York, 1925 and 1928), p. 61, ill.; L. Venturi, *Cézanne – son art, son oeuvre* (Paris, 1936), No. 601, ill.; A. C. Barnes and V. de Mazia, *The Art of Cézanne* (New York), 1939, No. 122, p. 414, p. 274, ill.; J. Rewald, "French Paintings in the Collection of Mr. and Mrs. John Hay Whitney," *The Connoisseur* (March-April, 1956), p. 138, ill.; J. Russell, "La collection Whitney," *L'Oeil* (May, 1958), p. 37, ill. in color.

THEODORE CHASSERIAU

Santa Barbara de Samanà, Santo Domingo, 1819-1856, Paris

A Creole, as were Degas, Gauguin, and Pissarro, Chassériau moved to Paris in 1822 when his diplomat father was transferred home. At the age of twelve his brilliance as a painter gained him entrance as a student into the studio of Ingres where he remained for four years until, in 1834, the master was named Director of the French Academy at Rome. The influence of Ingres' Neo-Classicism is mixed, in Chassériau, with the rival, Romantic style of Delacroix, producing a simultaneously eclectic and original style. He became, before his premature death at thirty-seven, a pivotal figure in the century combining, in Gautier's words, Hellenic purity with Oriental exoticism. His own influence is to be seen in the works of Puvis de Chavannes, Gustave Moreau, and Odilon Redon.

14. NUDE, 1842

Oil on canvas, 39 x 30⅜
Signed and dated, lower right: T. Ch. 1842
Lent by Mr. Cecil D. Kaufmann, Washington, D.C.

EX-COLL: Rodolphe Rey, Algiers.

EXHIBITIONS: *Exposition Chassériau*, Paris, Musée de l'Orangerie (1933), No. 23, p. 13; *Exposition d'oeuvres de Théodore Chassériau*, Algiers, Musée national des Beaux-Arts (March-May, 1936), No. 5; *Man, Glory, Jest and Riddle: A Survey of the Human Form through the Ages*, San Francisco, California Palace of the Legion of Honor (November 10, 1964-January 3, 1965), No. 156; *Romantics and Realists*, New York, Wildenstein (April 7-May 7, 1966), pl. 1.

LITERATURE: J. Alazard, "Théodore Chassériau," *Gazette des Beaux-Arts* (January, 1933), p. 55, fig. 9; J. Ashbery, "The Romance of Reality," *Art News* (April, 1966), Vol. 65, No. 2, p. 30.

JEAN-BAPTISTE CAMILLE COROT

Paris, 1796-1875, Ville-d'Avray

In 1822 Corot began to study painting with the classical landscape painters Michallon and J. V. Bertin. He went to Italy three years later and absorbed more of the classical tradition of landscape, a tradition which he was never to forsake. He returned to Paris in 1828 to establish a pattern of working in the country, out-of-doors, during the summer and returning to his studio for the winter preparation of his large Salon pieces. He returned to Italy twice, in 1834 and again in 1845. Although he did not offer formal training, Corot had, by 1850, a number of disciples. Despite the prominence of his misty Claudesque landscapes and his growing preoccupation with figure studies his main impact on younger artists came from his paintings done from nature.

15. CASTEL SAN ANGELO, 1826-1827

(View of Rome)
Oil on paper backed with canvas, 8⅝ x 15
Marked: *Vente/Corot,* lower left
The California Palace of the Legion of Honor, San Francisco
Collis P. Huntington Memorial Collection (1935.2)

EX-COLL: Charles Tillot, Paris, 1887; Dr. Dievlafoy, Paris; Wildenstein, New York.

EXHIBITIONS: *Tableaux par Corot,* Paris, Hôtel Drouot (1875), No. 24, ill.; *L'exposition centennale,* Paris, No. 156, ill.; *Corot-Daumier,* New York, Museum of Modern Art (1930), No. 2, ill.; *Exhibition of French Paintings from the Fifteenth Century to the Present Day,* San Francisco, California Palace of the Legion of Honor (1934), No. 78, ill.; *French Painting from David to Toulouse-Lautrec,* New York, Metropolitan Museum of Art (1941), No. 13; *Corot, 1796-1875,* Philadelphia, Museum of Art (1946), No. 2, ill.; *French Paintings: 1100-1900,* Pittsburgh, Carnegie Institute (1951); *De David à Toulouse-Lautrec: chefs-d'oeuvre des collections américaines,* Paris, Musée de l'Orangerie (1955), No. 7, ill. pl. 22; *J. B. C. Corot,* Washington, D. C., The Phillips Gallery (1957), No. 3, ill.; *Corot,* Chicago, Art Institute (1960), No. 13, ill.

LITERATURE: Alfred Robaut, *L'Oeuvre de Corot* (Paris, 1905), Vol. 2, No. 70, ill.; John Rewald "Corot sources: The Camera Tells," *Art News* (November 15, 1942), Vol. 41, pp. 11-13, ill.; *California Palace of the Legion of Honor Bulletin* (April, 1944), Vol. 2, p. 2, ill.; *California Palace of the Legion of Honor Bulletin* (February, 1946), Vol. 3, p. 86, ill.

JEAN-BAPTISTE CAMILLE COROT

Paris, 1796-1875, Ville-d'Avray

16. LA LISEUSE À LA JUPE DE VELOURS

(The Reader)
Oil on canvas, 29⅝ x 16½
Signed, lower right: Corot
The Minneapolis Institute of Arts, Minneapolis
Bequest of Mrs. Egil Boeckmann (67.31.2)

EX-COLL: C. Dutilleux, 1874; A. Robaut; M. Sedelmeyer, 1890; J. J. Hill.

EXHIBITIONS: *Vente C. Dutilleux* (1874), No. 27; *Exposition Ecole des Beaux Arts* (1875), No. 102; *Exhibition,* Durand-Ruel (1878), No. 101; *The Serene World of Corot,* New York, Wildenstein (1942), No. 49; *Anniversary Exhibition,* Minneapolis, Institute of Arts (1958).

LITERATURE: P. Burty, *Exposition de l'oeuvre de Corot* (Paris, 1875); A. Robaut, *L'oeuvre de Corot* (Paris, 1899), Vol. III, No. 1554; M. Hamel, *Corot et son oeuvre* (Paris, 1905), p. 27; W. Genfel, *Corot und Troyon* (Leipzig, 1906), p. 57, ill.; E. Waldman, "Tableaux français dans les collections privées américans," *Kunst und Kunstler* (November, 1910), pp. 85-97; J. Meier-Graefe, *Camille Corot* (Munich, 1913), p. 143; J. Meier-Graefe, *Camille Corot* (Berlin, 1930), pl. CXIV *(Madchen in Sammetrock);* Bernheim de Villers, *Corot, peintre de figures* (Paris, 1930), p. 60, ill. pl. 248; *Minneapolis Institute of Arts Bulletin* (April-June, 1958), Vol. XLVII, p. 26; *Gazette des Beaux-Arts* (February, 1968), p. 77, No. 284; *Art Quarterly* (Spring, 1968), p. 94, ill. p. 104.

JEAN-BAPTISTE CAMILLE COROT

Paris, 1796-1875, Ville-d'Avray

17. LE PORT DE LA ROCHELLE, 1851

(The Harbour of La Rochelle)
Oil on canvas, 19⅞ x 28¼
Signed, lower right: Corot
Yale University Art Museum, New Haven
Bequest of Stephen Carlton Clark, B.A. 1903 (1961.18.14)

EX-COLL: Alfred Robaut, Paris (acquired from the artist at the exhibition in Arras, 1868); C. Dutilleux, 1874; Durand-Ruel, New York; Baron Nathaniel de Rothschild; Baron Léonine Henri de Rothschild; Wildenstein & Company, New York; Stephen C. Clark, New York.

EXHIBITIONS: *Salon*, Paris (1852), No. 283, Rouen (1856), Toulouse (1865), Amiens (1868), Arras (1868); *Exposition posthume . . .* Paris, Ecole des Beaux-Arts (1875), No. 97; *Exposition rétrospective*, Paris, Galerie Durand-Ruel (1878), No. 95; *Exposition universelle, centennale de l'art français*, Paris (1889), No. 155; *Masterpieces of Art*, New York World's Fair (1940), No. 253, ill.; *Corot*, Philadelphia, Museum of Art (1946), No. 26 (colorplate); *French Paintings of the Latter Half of the XIXth Century from the Collections of Alumni and Friends of Yale*, New Haven, Yale University Art Gallery (1950), No. 4, ill.; *A Collector's Taste*, New York, M. Knoedler (1954), No. 5, ill.; *De David à Toulouse-Lautrec*, Paris, Musée de l'Orangerie (1955), No. 8, ill.; *Paintings and Drawings and Sculpture Collected by Yale Alumni*, New Haven, Yale University Art Gallery (1960), No. 39, ill.; *Corot*, Chicago, Art Institute (1960), No. 76; *In the Light of Vermeer: 500 Years of Painting*, Mauritshuis, The Hague (1966).

LITERATURE: Th. Sylvestre, *Histoire des artistes vivants* (Paris, 1856), p. 404; H. Dumesnil, *Corot* (Paris, 1875), No. 58, p. 126; A. Robaut, *L'oeuvre de Corot* (Paris, 1904-1906), Vol. I, pp. 128, 137; II, p. 230, No. 669, ill.; Meier-Graefe, *Corot* (Berlin, 1930), p. 69; E. Faure, *Corot* (Paris, 1931), p. 50, ill. p. 53; Courthion, *Corot, raconté par lui-même et par ses amis* (Geneva, 1946), I, p. 60; II, p. 145; D. Baud-Boyy, *Corot* (Geneva, 1957), p. 220; A. Coquis, *Corot et la critique contemporaine* (Paris, 1959), p. 61; *Yale Art Gallery Bulletin* (December, 1962), Vol. 28, ill. p. 13.

GUSTAVE COURBET

Orans, 1819-1877, Tour du Peitz

In opposition to Classicism and Romanticism which had held the aesthetic and artistic battlefield of the early 19th century, Courbet offered something else; in the '50s and '60s, he was the founder and leader of the Realists. Though it is difficult to establish a definition of "Realism," one can say that, in the depiction of subject matter, it was naturalistic; in regard to idea, it supported the modern real world in contradiction to Classicist and Romanticist efforts to raise man above everyday life. Courbet himself was unpopular because of his sharp tongue and inordinate conceit. In addition, he was thought to be politically dangerous. Still, amongst the artists, the power and honesty of his works and the force of his personality were a great influence. For the artists, he offered an alternative to the two main choices of the century. In an important sense this was the opportunity to begin again — for example, the Impressionists' devotion to ordinary, non-heroic subject matter can be traced to Courbet's Realism.

18. LA SIESTE, 1868

(The Rest: Haying Season)
Oil on canvas, 91½ x 107½
Signed and dated, lower right: G. Courbet 68
Musée du Petit Palais, Paris

EX-COLL: Acquired by the City of Paris, Courbet Sale, 1881.

EXHIBITIONS: *Exposition des oeuvres de M. G. Courbet*, Paris, Rond-Point du Pont de l'Alma (1867), No. 19; *Salon*, Paris (1869), No. 572; *Exposition centennale de l'art français, 1800-1889*, Paris, Grand Palais des Champs-Elysées (1900), No. 144; *Chefs d'oeuvre de l'art français*, Paris, Palais National des Arts (1937), No. 279; *De David à Cézanne*, Brussels, Palais des Beaux-Arts (1947), No. 72, ill. pl. 41; *G. Courbet*, Copenhagen, Statens Museum for Kunst (1949), No. 24, ill. pl. IV; *G. Courbet*, Paris, Petit Palais (1955); *French XIXth Century Painting*, Munich, Haus der Kunst (1958).

LITERATURE: Castagnary, *Salons* (1892), I, p. 357; A. Estignard, *G. Courbet, sa vie et ses oeuvres* (Besancon, 1897), p. 166, ill. p. 132; G. Riat, *G. Courbet, peintre* (Paris, 1906), pp. 246-248, 371, ill.; L. Bénédite, J. Laran, and Gaston Dreyfus, *Courbet* (Paris, 1912), p. 94, ill. pl. XXXIX; Th. Duret, *Courbet* (Paris, 1918), pp. 73, 81, ill. pl. XXXIII; Ch. Leger, *Courbet et son temps* (Paris, 1948), p. 117; P. Courthion, *Courbet raconté par lui-même . . .* (Geneva, 1950), II, ill.; G. Mack, *Gustave Courbet* (London, 1951), p. 211, ill. pl. 49.

THOMAS COUTURE

Senslis, 1815-1879 Villiers-le-Bel

Couture was a pupil, first of Gros and then of Paul Delaroche. He received a Prix de Rome in 1837 and first exhibited in the Salon of 1838, although his greatest public success came with *Romans of the Decadence* of 1847. He was a history and genre painter who eclectically combined the elements of 18th-century Venetian painting with the prevailing Neo-Classicism. Couture was an influential teacher at the Ecole des Beaux-Arts and his studio was widely popular. He taught Edouard Manet and Puvis de Chavannes as well as the German artist, Feuerbach. Couture was appointed court painter to Napoleon III, and while on the Salon jury, he rejected the works of his former pupil, Manet.

19. THE FALCONER, 1855

Oil on canvas, 51 x 38½
Signed, lower left (on balustrade): T. COUTURE
The Toledo Museum of Art, Toledo
Gift of Edward Drummond Libbey (54.78)

EX-COLL: Deforge, 1855-1857; Faure, Paris; Geheimrat von Ravené, Marquard, Germany, by 1869; Galerie Eduard Schulte, Berlin, 1913; Thannhauser Galleries, Berlin, 1927; Justin K. Thannhauser, New York, 1945.

EXHIBITIONS: *Exposition universelle,* Paris (1855), No. 2820; *Die Internationale Kunstaustellung,* Munich (1869); *Grosse Kunstaustellung,* Dresden (1912); *Grande exposition de chefs d'oeuvre de l'art français,* Berlin, Thannhauser Galleries (1927), No. 56, ill. pl. 43.

LITERATURE: Clara Clement and Lawrence Hutton, *Artists of the 19th Century* (Boston, 1884), Vol. I, p. 166; C. H. Stranahan, *A History of French Painting* (New York, 1888), p. 292; Clarence Cook, *Art and Artists of Our Time* (New York, 1888), Vol. I, pp. 187, 190; Richard Muther, *History of Modern Painting* (London, 1895), Vol. I, p. 406; W. von Seidlitz, *Monumentalmalerei eine Einführung in die Grosse Kunstaustellung* (Dresden, 1912); Thieme-Becker, "Thomas Couture," *Allgemeines Lexicon der Bildenden Kunstler,* p. 5; Isabella Errera, *Répertoire des peintures datées* (Brussels, Paris, 1920), p. 682 (1855); Camille Mauclair, *Thomas Couture* (Paris, 1932), ill. facing p. 25, preface IX, XI, pp. 34, 35, 154; Georges Bertauts-Couture, *Thomas Couture* (Paris, 1932), p. 33, ill. p. 25; Denys Sutton, "Nineteenth-Century Painting; Trends and Cross-Currents," *Apollo,* (December, 1967), Vol. 86, No. 70, p. 493, ill. fig. 20, p. 492.

HENRI-EDMOND CROSS

Douai, 1856-1910, Lavandou

Cross studied at the Ecole des Beaux-Arts in Lille and with the artist Bonvin. He painted somewhat in the Divisionist style after 1884 although he did not fully adopt the Neo-Impressionist technique until the year Georges Seurat died, 1891. He was one of the founders of the Société des Indépendants and exhibited with them regularly after 1884. With Signac, he developed the second phase of Neo-Impressionism which was to be important in the early 20th-century to the Fauves and Cubists.

20. LA RONDE, 1895

(Excursion)
Oil on canvas, 45¾ x 64¾
Lent by Mr. Walter P. Chrysler, Jr., New York

EX-COLL: Dr. A. Roudinesco, Paris.

EXHIBITIONS: *Société des artistes indépendants*, Paris (1895), No. 318; *Seurat et ses amis*, Paris, Les Expositions des Beaux Arts et de *La Gazette des Beaux-Arts* (December, 1933-January, 1934), No. 16; *H. E. Cross*, Paris, Galerie Bernheim-Jeune (1937), No. 42; *Il Divisionismo*, Venice, Biennale di Venezia (Summer, 1952), No. 9; *French Paintings 1789-1929 from the Collection of Walter P. Chrysler, Jr.*, Dayton, Ohio, The Dayton Art Institute (March 25-May 22, 1960), No. 77; *The Outline and the Dot, Two Aspects of Post-Impressionism*, Dallas, Museum of Fine Arts (March 4-25, 1962), No. 35.

LITERATURE: *Seurat et ses amis* (Paris, December, 1933-January, 1934), No. 16; Biennale di Venezia, *Il Divisionismo* (Venice, Summer, 1952), No. 9; The Dayton Art Institute, *French Paintings 1789-1929 from the Collection of Walter P. Chrysler, Jr.*, (Dayton, Ohio, 1960), Catalogue Notes, No. 77, pp. 85, 132; Dallas Museum of Fine Arts, *The Outline and the Dot, Two Aspects of Post-Impressionism* (Dallas, 1962), No. 35.

HONORE VICTORIN DAUMIER

Marseille, 1808-1879, Valmondois

The son of a glazier and would-be poet, Daumier passed the latter portion of his childhood in Paris where his family moved in 1816. His professional training for an artistic career was minimal. Brief study in classes at the Académie Suisse gave him a mastery of figure drawing. However, as a painter he was largely self-taught and his earliest successes were as a lithographer. Work from 1830-1872 for the weeklies *La Caricature* and, later, *Le Charivari* established him as the outstanding satirist of bourgeois life and the political scene of his day. Meissonier exerted a considerable influence on the iconography of his paintings, as did Millet. His career as a painter, however, was plagued by lack of public success and increasing blindness following the year 1872. A sketchiness of style, lack of finish, and a bold and powerful way of drawing with paint are the hallmarks of his works.

21. L'HOMME À LA CORDE, ca. 1858-1860

(The Man on a Rope)
Oil on canvas, 43¼ x 28⅜
The National Gallery of Canada, Ottawa (5061)

EX-COLL: N. Hazard, Ourrouy, Paris, 1919; Barbazanges; van Wisselingh, Amsterdam (1928-33); H. S. Southam, Ottawa (1950).

EXHIBITIONS: *Exposition de peinture française*, Basle, Société des Beaux-Arts (1921), No. 55; *Cent ans de peinture française*, Amsterdam, Galerie van Wisselingh (1928), No. 21, ill.; *Daumier*, London, Tate Gallery (1961), No. 80; *Art in the Making*, Waterville, Maine, Colby College Art Museum (1966).

LITERATURE: Klossowski, *Daumier* (1908), No. 231 (wrong measurements); *Catalogue de la Vente Hazard* (Paris, 1919), No. 105; Fuchs, *Daumier*, (1927), No. 49; "Nachtrag" (1930), No. 63, pl. 290; *From David to Courbet* (Detroit, 1950), No. 47; Adhémar, *Daumier* (1954), No. 125; *Architectural Review* (1961), Vol. 130, p. 203; Hubbard, *European Paintings in Canadian Collections* (1962), Vol. II, p. 152; Maison, *Daumier* (1968), Vol. I, No. 1-122, p. 116, pl. 174.

JACQUES-LOUIS DAVID

Paris, 1748-1825, Brussels

David had a baffling artistic-political career: court painter to Louis XVI, principal painter of the French Revolution, first painter to the Emperor Napoleon, he died in exile in Brussels out of favor with the restored Bourbons. Such a life makes little political sense; artistically, however, it did. He gave nascent Neo-Classical tendencies in art a context and permanent form which influenced French art for the next hundred years. Deserting the "pretty" and elegant Rococo, he revolutionized art, transforming it into a serious, lofty, and noble style fit for a new class which was to adjust the wrongs of the past. His style was based upon the calm, heroic, republican spirit he saw in the antique. His Neo-Classical manner spoke of honor and loyalty and had the effect of confirming the bourgeoisie's position as the purveyor of political virtue. David had an immense influence upon the artists of his day in his ideas as well as through his technique.

22. PORTRAIT OF GÉNÉRAL GÉRARD, 1816

(Count Etienne Maurice Gérard, Marshal of France, 1773-1852)
Oil on canvas, 77⅝ x 53⅝
Signed and dated, lower left: L. DAVID/1816/BRUX
The Metropolitan Museum of Art, New York
Purchase, 1965, Rogers and Fletcher Funds,
Bequest of Mary Wetmore Shively in memory of
her husband Henry L. Shively, M.D.

EX-COLL: M. le comte d'Archiac, Château de Villers Saint-Paul (Oise).

LITERATURE: A. Thomé, *Vie de David* (Paris, 1826), pp. 144-45, 166; Jean du Seigneur, "Appendice à la notice de P. Chaussard sur David," *Revue universelle des arts,* (1863-64), Vol. XVIII, p. 367; Jules David, *Le peintre Louis David* (Paris, 1880), p. 649; Richard Cantinelli, *Jacques-Louis David* (Paris and Brussels, 1930), No. 139, p. 113; Klaus Holma, *David, son évolution et son style* (Paris, 1940), No. 145, p. 129; P. A. Coupin, *Essai J. L. David* (Paris, 1827), p. 57; Miette de Villars, *Mémoires de David* (Paris, 1850), pp. 207-208; E. J. Delécluse, *Louis David, son école et son temps* (Paris, 1855), p. 367; Louis Hautecoeur, *Louis David* (Paris, 1954), p. 264.

EDGAR-HILAIRE-GERMAIN DEGAS

Paris, 1834-1917, Paris

Born of wealthy upper-class parents, Degas' natural milieu was one of intellectualism, conservatism, and good taste. An early decision to follow an artistic career led to training in the academic tradition of Neo-Classicism at the studio of Louis Lamothe, a pupil of Ingres. This was followed by a period of study in Italy which confirmed his natural propensities for drawing and made draughtsmanship the core of his art. An Impressionist painter who contributed to all but one of the eight Impressionist exhibitions, Degas was never drawn to *plein air* painting nor to the instantaneous recording of visual impressions. His subjects are almost exclusively urban in origin, the object of his most passionate research being the human animal in motion. His carefully composed canvases reveal his intelligence, objectivity, and subtle focusing of the viewer's attention.

23. CLASSE DE BALLET, ca. 1880

(The Ballet Class)
Oil on canvas, 32⅛ x 30⅛
Signed, lower left: Degas
Lent by the Commissioners of Fairmont Park, W. P. Wilstach
Collection, Courtesy of the Philadelphia Museum of Art,
Philadelphia (W'37-2-1)

EX-COLL: Mary Cassatt; Mrs. William Potter Wear; Mrs. Plunket Stewart; Elise Cassatt Stewart Simmons.

EXHIBITIONS: *Annual*, Philadelphia, Museum of Art (1920); *Impressionism: The Figure Painters*, Philadelphia, Museum of Art (1934); *Degas*, Philadelphia, Museum of Art (1936), No. 35, ill. p. 87; *Degas*, Paris, Musée de l'Orangerie (1937), No. 30, ill.; *Diamond Jubilee*, Philadelphia, Museum of Art (1950-1951), No. 75; *Director's Choice*, Sarasota, Florida, Ringling Museum (1955); *Degas*, Los Angeles, County Art Museum (1958), No. 29, ill.; *Manet, Degas, Morisot and Cassatt*, Baltimore, Museum of Art (1962), No. 42, ill. p. 13.

LITERATURE: A. Vollard, *Degas, an Intimate Portrait* (New York, 1927), ill. fig. 26; Philadelphia, Museum of Art, *62 Annual Report* (1938), ill. p. 12; P. A. Lemoisne, *Degas et son oeuvre* (Paris, 1946), Vol. II, p. 264, No. 479, ill. p. 265; T. Fermor, "Paintings I Like at the Art Museum," *PGW News* (Philadelphia, November, 1962), ill. p. 15, ref. p. 15.

EDGAR-HILAIRE-GERMAIN DEGAS

Paris, 1834-1917, Paris

24. DEGAS' FATHER LISTENING TO PAGANS PLAYING
THE GUITAR, ca. 1872

Oil on canvas, 31½ x 24⅞
Not signed or dated
Museum of Fine Arts, Boston
Bequest of John T. Spaulding (48.533)

EX-COLL: Degas family; M. Henri Fèvre, Nice (1925); Durand-Ruel; Mr. John T. Spaulding (1926).

EXHIBITIONS: *Degas*, Paris, Georges Petit (1924), No. 8; *French Painting of the 19th and 20th Centuries*, Cambridge, Massachusetts, Fogg Art Museum (1929), No. 26, ill. pl. XVII; *Century of Progress*, Chicago, Art Institute (1934), No. 201, ill. pl. XLI; *Degas*, New York, Marie Harriman (1934), No. 8; *Degas*, Philadelphia, Pennsylvania Museum of Art (1936), No. 18, ill.; *Degas*, New York, Durand-Ruel (1937), No. 5, ill.; *World's Fair Exhibition*, New York (1940), No. 272, ill.; *19th Century French Paintings from American Collections*, Paris, Musée de l'Orangerie, No. 19, ill.; *Degas*, Los Angeles, County Art Museum (1958), No. 22, ill. color; *Degas*, New York, Wildenstein (1960), No. 18, ill.

LITERATURE: G. Moore, *Impressions and Opinions* (1891), p. 320; G. Moore, *Modern Painting* (1910), p. 275; G. Migeon, "L'oeuvre de Degas," *Beaux-Arts*, II (April 15, 1924), p. 114; P. A. Lemoisne, "Edgar Degas," *Revue de l'art* (June, 1924), p. 22; P. Hendy, "Degas and the de Gas," *Boston Museum of Fine Arts Bulletin* (June, 1932), Vol. XXX, p. 44; V. Nirdlinger, "Some Family Portraits by Degas," *Parnassus* (March, 1932), Vol. IV, p. 14, ill.; M. Guérin, "Le Portrait du chanteur Pagans et de M. de Gas père," *Bulletin des musées de France* (1933), Vol. V, p. 35; P. A. Lemoisne, *Degas et son oeuvre* (1946), Vol. II, No. 256, ill.; D. Catton Rich, *Degas* (1951), p. 46, ill. in color; P. Cabanne, *Edgar Degas* (1958), pl. 35.

EDGAR-HILAIRE-GERMAIN DEGAS

Paris, 1834-1917, Paris

25. LA FILLE DE JEPHTE, ca. 1860

(The Daughter of Jephthah)
Oil on canvas, 77 x 117½
Signed, lower left: Degas
Smith College Museum of Art, Northampton, Massachusetts (1933:9)

EX-COLL: Degas; Carlos Baca-Flor.

EXHIBITIONS: *Degas*, Northampton, Smith College Museum of Art (November 28, December 18, 1933), No. 5, cover ill.; *French Exhibition*, Rochester, University of Rochester (March, 1935); *One Hundred Years of French Painting*, Kansas City, William Rockhill Nelson Gallery of Art (March-April, 1935), No. 5, ill. pl. V; *Degas*, Philadelphia, Pennsylvania Museum of Art (November, 1936), No. 7, ill. p. 59; *Degas*, Paris, Musée de l'Orangerie (March-May, 1937), No. 3, pp. 14, 15, ill. pl. 2; *Degas*, New York, Wildenstein (April 7-May 7, 1960), No. 7, ill.; *Ingres and Degas, Two Classic Draftsmen*, Cambridge, Fogg Art Museum (April 24-May 20, 1961), No. 17, p. 28.

LITERATURE: P. A. Lemoisne, *Degas: L'art de notre temps* (Paris, 1912), p. 30; *Catalogue vente Degas*, Georges Petit Galleries (Paris, May, 1918), Vol. I, No. 6a, ill.; Paul Lafond, *Degas* (Paris, 1918), Vol. I, ill. p. 17, Vol. II (Paris, 1919), p. 2; Henri Hertz, *Degas* (Paris, 1920), p. 92; Paul Jamot, *Degas* (Paris, 1924), p. 31; Gustave Coquiot, *Degas* (Paris, 1924), p. 108; J. B. Mason, *The Life and Work of Edgar Degas* (New York, 1927), p. 10; *Smith College Alumnae Quarterly* (February, 1934), p. 166, ill.; *Smith College Museum of Art Bulletin* (1934), pp. 3-8, ill. pp. 2, 6, 7, and 8; Eleanor Mitchell, "La Fille de Jephte par Degas," *Gazette des Beaux-Arts* (October, 1937), pp. 175-189, ill. pp. 176-189; P. A. Lemoisne, *Degas et son oeuvre* (Paris, 1947), No. 94.

FERDINAND-VICTOR-EUGENE DELACROIX
Charenton-Saint-Maurice, 1798-1863, Paris

Born near Paris in 1798, Delacroix entered the studio of Guérin in 1815 and later met Géricault and Bonington. He was the major figure in the Romantic movement in France. His trips to England in 1825 and North Africa in 1832 had a great impact on his work, particularly in his choice of strong colors and literary and exotic subjects. His color theories ultimately influenced the Impressionists and Seurat. Delacroix fought against the classical tradition in French painting which then prevailed, and his works were often subject to attack by critics. Although he had shown in the Salon from 1822, he was not elected to the Institute until 1857.

26. LA BATAILLE DE TAILLEBOURG (Study), ca. 1834-1837

(The Battle of Taillebourg)
Oil on canvas, 20⅞ x 26⅛
Musée du Louvre, Paris

EX-COLL: Delacroix Sale, Paris, February 17, 1864, No. 57; M. Haro; Baron Vitta; Musée du Louvre, Gift of Baron Vitta, 1924.

EXHIBITIONS: *Delacroix*, Paris, Galerie Martinet (1864), No. 47; *Delacroix*, Paris, Musée du Louvre (1930), No. 82; *Peintures et dessins de Delacroix*, Paris, Atelier de Delacroix (1934), No. 22; *Gros, ses amis, ses élèves*, Paris, Petit Palais (1936), No. 830; *Capolavori dell'ottocento francese*, Rome (1955), No. 37, Florence (1955), No. 35; *Centenaire de Delacroix*, Paris, Musée du Louvre (1963), No. 234; *Le Romantisme dans la peinture française*, Moscow, Pushkin Museum, and Léningrad, Hermitage (1968-1969), No. 32.

LITERATURE: A. Moreau, *Eugène Delacroix et son oeuvre* (Paris, 1873), p. 312; A. Robaut, *L'oeuvre complet d'Eugène Delacroix* (Paris, 1885), No. 650; E. Moreau-Nélaton, *Delacroix raconté par lui-même* (Paris, 1916), Vol. I, p. 180; J. Guiffrey, "L'esquisse de la bataille de Taillebourg," *Beaux-Arts* (July 15, 1924), pp. 215-216; R. Escholier, *Delacroix* (Paris, 1927), Vol. II, pp. 233-234; Ch. Sterling and H. Adhémar, *La peinture au musée du Louvre, l'ecole française, le XIXe siècle* (Paris, 1959), No. 682; pl. 241; *Eugène Delacroix, Journal de Delacroix* (Paris, 1960), Vol. III, p. 313; R. Escholier, *Eugène Delacroix* (Paris, 1963), p. 113; M. Sérullaz, *Eugène Delacroix, Memorial* (Paris, 1963), No. 230; H. Huyghe, *Delacroix ou le combat solitaire* (Paris, 1964), p. 332, fig. 18, pl. 245.

FERDINAND-VICTOR-EUGENE DELACROIX

Charenton-Saint-Maurice, 1798-1863, Paris

27. LES CONVULSIONNAIRES DE TANGER

(The Fanatics of Tangiers)
Oil on canvas, 38⅝ x 51¾
Signed and dated, lower right: Eug. Delacroix, 183(8?)
Lent by Mr. J. Jerome Hill, New York

EX-COLL: Van Isacker; M. Jourdan, 1852; M. Mela, 1855; Marquis du Lau; Edwards, 1869; M. Balensi (or Fedor), 1881; M. Faure, 1885; George I. Seney, 1889; James J. Hill, 1895.

EXHIBITIONS: *Salon,* Paris (1838), No. 457; *Exposition universelle,* Paris (1855), No. 2933; *Exhibition,* Paris, Durand-Ruel (1878), No. 145; *Exhibition,* Paris (1885), No. 77; *Barye Exhibition,* New York (1889-1890), No. 581; *Chicago World's Fair* (1934), No. 8; *Exhibition,* Paris, Louvre (1930), No. 85; *New York World's Fair* (1940), No. 248; *Exhibition of Private Collectors,* Minneapolis, Institute of Arts (1941); *James J. Hill Collection,* Minneapolis, Institute of Arts (1958).

LITERATURE: A. Robaut, *L'oeuvre complet d'Eugene Delacroix* (Paris, 1885), p. 179, p. 662; E. Moreau-Nélaton, *Eugène Delacroix raconté par lui-même* (Paris, 1916), pp. 163-164; J. Meier-Graefe, *Eugène Delacroix* (Munich, 1922), p. 128; R. Escholier, *Delacroix, 1832-1848* (Paris, 1927), Vol. II, p. 72, ill.; *Minneapolis Institute of Arts Bulletin* (March 6, 1943), No. 32, pp. 34-37, ill.; J. Lassaigne, *Eugène Delacroix* (New York, 1950), p. 21, ill.; *Minneapolis Institute of Arts Bulletin* (1958), No. 2, p. 23, ill.; R. Huyghe, *Delacroix* (London, 1963), pp. 227, 293, 303, 418, ill. in color, p. 288, detail.

FERDINAND-VICTOR-EUGENE DELACROIX

Charenton-Saint-Maurice, 1798-1863, Paris

28. FEMMES TURQUES AU BAIN, 1854

(Turkish Women Bathing)
Oil on canvas, 36¼ x 30½
Signed and dated, lower left: Eug. Delacroix
Wadsworth Atheneum, Hartford
The Ella Gallup Sumner and Mary Catlin Sumner Collection (1952.300)

EX-COLL: John Saulnier, Paris, 1886; Ferdinand Blumenthal, Paris; Count Pecci-Blunt; Mr. and Mrs. R. L.; Paul Rosenberg, New York.

EXHIBITIONS: *Delacroix*, Paris, Ecole des Beaux-Arts (1885), No. 190; *Chefs d'oeuvre de l'ecole française*, Paris (1910), No. 56; *Cent chefs d'oeuvre de l'école de Paris*, Paris (1911); *Delacroix*, Paris, Musée du Louvre (1930), No. 165; *Delacroix*, Paris, Musée de l'Orangerie (1933), No. 195; *The Painting of France since the French Revolution*, San Francisco, M. H. de Young Museum (December, 1940), No. 35; *The Romantic Circle*, Hartford, Wadsworth Atheneum (1952), No. 33, ill. frontispiece; *De David à Toulouse-Lautrec, chefs-d'oeuvre des collections américaines*, Paris, Musée de l'Orangerie (1955), No. 26, ill. pl. 15; *The Venetian Tradition*, Cleveland, Museum of Art (1956-57), No. 10, ill. pl. LI; *Centenary of the Death of Eugène Delacroix*, Paris, Palais du Louvre (1963), No. 451.

LITERATURE: A. Moreau, *Delacroix* (1873), p. 274; A. Robaut, *Delacroix* (1885), No. 1240; R. Escholier, *Delacroix* (1929), III, p. 192; L. Hourticq, *Delacroix* (1930), p. 147, ill.; Riat, *Delacroix: Journal of Eugène Delacroix*, trans. Walter Pach (1937), pp. 380-381; *Prométhée*, Vol. 20 (May, 1939), p. 29, ill.; M. G. Michel, *Les grandes époques de la peinture moderne* (1945), p. 33, ill. *Wadsworth Atheneum Bulletin* (November, 1952), No. 35, p. 1, ill.; Corrado Maltese, *Delacroix* (Rome, 1964), ill. pl. 90.

PAUL DELAROCHE

Paris, 1797-1856, Paris

As a young man Delaroche studied under Baron Gros before making his debut in the Salon of 1822. Delaroche's main forte was history painting which he treated in a distinctly sentimental and genre manner. The human interest was usually greater than the formal one, and the artist's subjects often dealt with scenes of misfortunes, especially those of the upper classes. Although not an unhappy-natured man, his was a sentimental and melancholy attitude which enjoyed popular acclaim. In 1837, however, two of his paintings received harsh criticism from the officials, and Delaroche renounced official painting entirely. He subsequently showed an increasing interest in portraiture and religious scenes while also maintaining his original interest in history painting.

29. LA JEUNE MARTYRE, 1855

(A Young Martyr at the Time of Diocletian)
Oil on canvas, 67⅛ x 58¼
Musée du Louvre, Paris

EX-COLL: Delaroche Sale, June, 1857; Musée du Louvre, Gift of Mlle Roud and of MM. Adolphe and Louis d'Eichtal, 1897.

EXHIBITIONS: *Exposition des oeuvres de Paul Delaroche*, Paris, Ecole des Beaux-Arts (1857), No. 53; *Le salon imaginaire*, Berlin, Académie des Arts (October-November, 1968), No. 31, ill. p. 119.

LITERATURE: J. Godde, *Catalogue raisonné de l'oeuvre de Paul Delaroche* (Paris, 1858), pl. 75; H. Vollmer, Thieme-Becker, *Allgemeines Lexicon der Bildenden Kunstler* (1913), Vol. VIII, p. 592; Brière (1924), No. 217a; Ch. Sterling and H. Adhémar, *La Peinture au musée du Louvre, l'école française, le XIXe siécle* (Paris, 1959), Vol. I, pl. 257.

MAURICE DENIS

Granville, 1870-1943, Paris

As a young man, Maurice Denis was influenced by Gauguin, Puvis de Chavannes, and Seurat. From these contacts and in conjunction with Sérusier
he became one of the principal theorists of the Symbolists. The Symbolists as an offshoot of Post-Impressionism were not so much interested in
describing things as in hinting at their meaning. Their connections with
French Symbolist literature are obvious, and theoretical writings about
this movement were essential to its acceptance. But Denis also painted,
producing a body of interesting work which itself gave important direction
to Symbolist painting. Later in his career his painting style and ideas
changed. During this period of his life he did decorative and religious
murals for public buildings and church interiors. It is for this work that
he is most widely known in France.

30. PROCESSION UNDER THE TREES, 1892

Oil on canvas, 22 x 39
Signed and dated, lower right: MAUD 92
Lent by Mr. and Mrs. Arthur G. Altschul, New York

EX-COLL: Roger Marx.

EXHIBITIONS: *Cinquième exposition des peintures impressionistes et symbolistes,*
La Barc de Boutteville (October 25-November 5, 1893), Offices of *La Dépêche de Toulouse*
(May, 1894); *Neo-Impressionists and Nabis in the Collection of Arthur G. Altschul,* New
Haven, Yale University Art Gallery (January 20-March 14, 1965), No. 22, ill. in color;
Van Gogh, Gauguin, and their Circle, New York, Christies (November 14-30, 1968), No. 6,
ill.

LITERATURE: *Neo-Impressionists & Nabis in the Collection of Arthur G. Altschul*
(New Haven, 1965), No. 22, ill.

VIRGILE-NARCISSE DIAZ DE LA PENA

Bordeaux, 1808-1876, Menton

Born of Spanish immigrant parents and orphaned in early youth, Diaz like so many artists of the 19th century began as a porcelain painter. His work reflects the taste of the Romantics and his life-long admiration for Delacroix. Diaz met Rousseau in the forest at Fontainebleau in 1837, which was also the year he exhibited his first Fontainebleau landscape. Although he exhibited rarely after the mid-century, his personal charm and rich tapestry-like canvases continued to attract admirers, among them Renoir, Pissarro, and Sisley, all of whom studied with Diaz.

31. VUE DANS LA FORÊT DE FONTAINEBLEAU, 1872
(View in the Fontainebleau Forest)
Oil on canvas, 28¼ x 36½
Signed, lower right: N. DIAZ — 1867
Musée des Beaux-Arts, Bordeaux

EXHIBITIONS: *Le vie du musée de 1939 à 1947*, Bordeaux, Musée de peinture (1947), No. 132; *Les trésors des musées de Bordeaux*, Tel'Aviv, Pavillion H. Rubenstein (1964), No. 81; *Landscapes of the 19th Century*, Dallas, Southern Methodist University (October 17-29, 1966).

LITERATURE: E. Vallet, *Catalogue des tableaux, sculptures, gravures, dessins exposés dans les galeries du musée de Bordeaux* (Bordeaux, 1881), No. 444; D. Alaux, *Musée de peinture de Bordeaux, Catalogue* (Bordeaux, 1910), No. 401; Ch. Saunier, *Bordeaux* (Paris, 1925) p. 127, ill. p. 125; *Musée de peinture et de sculpture de Bordeaux* (Belgrade, 1933), No. 241.

PAUL-GUSTAVE DORE

Strasbourg, 1832-1883, Paris

Doré studied at the Munich Academy and with E. Reichel in Dresden. He moved to Paris in 1847 and soon gained fame as an illustrator for *Le Journal pour Rire*. He was a noted lithographer and illustrator who in his lifetime illustrated almost ninety books of which the most famous were *Rabelais* in 1854 and Dante's *Inferno*. Doré considered himself primarily a painter, and although he exhibited at the Salon as early as 1851, most of his paintings date from after 1870. He painted landscapes and large compositions based on religious and historical themes.

32. THE SCOTTISH HIGHLANDS, 1875

Oil on canvas, 42¾ x 72⅛
Signed and dated, lower left: Gve. Dore 1875
The Toledo Museum of Art, Toledo
Gift of Arthur J. Secor (22.108)

EX-COLL: Arthur A. Crosby; Goupil and Company, New York.

LITERATURE: *Toledo Museum News* (October, 1922), No. 42; Blake-More Godwin, *European Paintings in the Toledo Museum* (1939), p. 214, ill. p. 215; Germain Viatte, "Gustave Doré peintre," *Art de France* (1964), Vol. 4, p. 350, ill. p. 349.

HENRI FANTIN-LATOUR
Grenoble, 1836-1904, Bure, Basse-Normandie

The son of a well-known portrait painter, Fantin-Latour first studied with his father, then subsequently did work in Paris with Lecoq de Boisbaudran and at the Ecole des Beaux-Arts. His true teacher, however, was the Louvre where he copied the works of the masters along with his friends, Manet, Whistler, and Berthe Morisot. Somewhat neglected due to the 20th-century's preoccupation with Impressionism and Post-Impressionism, Latour was nonetheless a gifted painter, esteemed in his own day by fellow artists. A painter's painter, he is best known for his flower pieces. Here realism is tempered by a strong romantic strain, and dazzling brushwork hints at depths of feeling beyond the surface beauty of individual blossoms. Intimacy and finesse align his works with those of his 18th-century predecessor, Chardin; his personal reveries sometimes suggest the rarer visions of Redon.

33. STILL LIFE: CORNER OF A TABLE

Oil on canvas, 38¼ x 49¼
Signed and dated, upper left: Fantin '73
The Art Institute of Chicago, Chicago
Ada Turnbull Hertle Fund

EX-COLL: G. Tempelaere; E. Lernoud, Paris; M. Mancini, Paris; César de Hauke, Paris.

EXHIBITIONS: *Salon*, Paris (1873), No. 557; *Exposition retrospective des oeuvres de Fantin-Latour*, Paris, Palais des Beaux-Arts (1906), No. 70; *Exposition du centenaire de Henri Fantin-Latour*, Grenoble (1936), No. 127; *De David à Toulouse-Lautrec, chefs-d'oeuvre des collections américaines*, Paris, Musée de l'Orangerie (1955), No. 27, ill. pl. 42.

LITERATURE: L. Bénédite, *L'oeuvre de Fantin-Latour* (Paris, 1906), ill.; A. Jullien, *Fantin-Latour, sa vie et ses amitiés* (Paris, 1911), No. 671, p. 76; *Exposition du centenaire de Henri Fantin-Latour* (Grenoble, 1936), No. 127; F. Gibson, *The Art of Henry Fantin-Latour: His Life and Work* (n.d.), pp. 117, 119, ill. pl. 34, p. 209; G. Kahn, *Fantin-Latour*, trans. W. Jackson (1927), pp. 22-26.

PAUL-JEAN FLANDRIN

Lyons, 1811-1902, Paris

Paul was the younger brother of Hippolyte Flandrin, the most widely respected religious painter of the first half of the century. Together they walked from Lyons to Paris to enter the atelier of Ingres, having completed early studies at the Ecole des Beaux-Arts in Lyons. Paul Flandrin specialized in landscape painting and during a trip to Italy in 1833-1838 became influenced by the technique of the 17th century, especially that of Poussin. His style is marked by an openness and a preoccupatoin with formal composition based on the picturesque. He was also known as a portraitist, and was further responsible for the completion of some of his brother's religious decorations at Nîmes which had been left unfinished at the time of the latter's death.

34. LES BORDS DU GARDON, PAYSAGE ANIMÉ, 1856

(By the Gardon River)
Oil on canvas, 36⅜ x 29⅛
Signed and dated, Paul Flandrin, 1856
Musée Ingres, Montauban, France (D.861.1)

EX-COLL: Acquired by the state in 1861.

EXHIBITIONS: *Salon*, Paris (1859); *Art lyonnais*, Lyons (1937); *Ingres et son temps*. Montauban (1967), No. 243; *Baudelaire et la critique*, Paris (1968).

LITERATURE: D. Ternois, *Guide du Musée*, p. 20; Jonathan Mayne, *The Mirror of Art* (Baudelaire critique d'art) (1955), ill. p. 344; D. Ternois, *Ingres et son temps* (1965), ill. No. 128.

JEAN-LOUIS FORAIN

Rheims, 1852-1931, Paris

Although Forain began his academic training under Gérome and Carpeaux, he soon became a member of the small group of Impressionists who met with Degas at the Nouvelle-Athènes. Forain was impressed by Manet's work, he knew Goya's etchings and admired Daumier. It was possibly the influence of Daumier which turned him from the sweetness of fleeting Parisian impressions to the more serious and sordid subjects dealing with social protest which now are his best known works. Establishing himself first as an illustrator in such papers as *La Cravache, Le Scapin,* and *La Vie Moderna,* Forain worked exclusively in oil only during the last ten years of his life.

35. COURTROOM SCENE

Oil on canvas, 23¾ x 28⅞
Signed, upper right: Forain
Museum of Art, Rhode Island School of Design, Providence, Rhode Island

PAUL GAUGUIN

Paris, 1848-1903, Dominica, Marquesas

Gauguin rejected Western civilization in favor of the magical simplicity of primitive cultures. He began painting as a hobby and from 1881 to 1886 exhibited with the Impressionists, showing works which did not differ greatly in style from those of Pissarro and Cézanne. Later work done at Pont Aven, along with Emil Bernard, led to the creation of the style known as Synthetism — a style which rejected Impressionism and drew upon medieval as well as primitive and non-Western art. In 1891 Gauguin left for Tahiti where he passed the major portion of his remaining life. His work shows an intense fusion of intellectual and formal sophistication with the more naive and mysterious aspects of primitivism. He influenced subsequent generations of artists by freeing art from reliance upon naturalistic, formal considerations.

36. I RARO TE OVIRI, 1891
    (Under the Pandanus)
    Oil on canvas, 28⅞ x 35¾
    Signed and dated, lower left: P. Gauguin '91; I raro te Oviri, lower right
    The Minneapolis Institute of Arts, Minneapolis
    William Hood Dunwoody Fund (41.4)

EX-COLL: Folkwang Museum, Essen; Marcel Kapfener, Paris; Justin K. Thannhauser, New York; Mr. and Mrs. Gilbert Fuller, Boston; Knoedler and Company, New York.

EXHIBITIONS: *Exhibition*, Berlin, Thannhauser Galerie (1928), No. 54; *Gauguin*, Cambridge, Fogg Art Museum (1936), No. 20; *Paintings and Sculpture from The Minneapolis Institute of Arts*, New York, The Knoedler Galleries (1957), Palm Beach, The Society of the Four Arts (1957); *Gauguin*, Chicago, Art Institute (1959), New York, Metropolitan Museum of Art (1959); *Gauguin and the Decorative Style*, New York, Solomon R. Guggenheim Museum (1966).

LITERATURE: Georges Daniel de Monfried, *Les lettres de Paul Gauguin* (Paris, 1918); W. Barth, *Paul Gauguin* (Basle, 1929), p. 123; Rotonchamp, *Gauguin* (Paris, 1934), p. 159; *Minneapolis Institute of Arts Bulletin* (April 4, 1942), Vol. XXXI, pp. 46-49; R. S. Davis, "Gauguin in Tahiti," *Minneapolis Institute of Arts Bulletin* (April 15, 1950), No. 39, p. 74; J. Rewald, *Post-Impressionism* (New York, 1965), pp. 528, 538, ill. p. 511; Peter Tomory, *Gauguin* (London, 1968), p. 10, fig. 5.

PAUL GAUGUIN

Paris, 1848-1903, Dominica, Marquesas

37. YELLOW CHRIST, 1889

Oil on canvas, 36¼ x 28⅞
Signed and dated, lower right: P. Gauguin 89
Albright-Knox Art Gallery, Buffalo

EX-COLL: Schuffenecker; Gustave Fayet, Igny; Paul Rosenberg, Paris; Captured by the Germans, recovered in 1946 and acquired by the Albright-Knox Gallery.

EXHIBITIONS: *Isms in Art Since 1800,* Providence, Museum of Art, Rhode Island School of Design (February 3-March 9, 1949), No. 24, p. 33; *Gauguin,* Paris, Musée de l'Orangerie (July, 1949), No. 14, Basle (December-January, 1950), No. 32, Lausanne (February-March, 1950); *French Painting 1100-1900,* Pittsburgh, Department of Fine Arts, Carnegie Institute (October 18-December 2, 1951), pl. No. 124; *The Two Sides of the Medal,* Detroit, Institute of Arts (September 28-November 6, 1954), No. 105; *Great French Paintings,* Chicago, Art Institute (January 20-February 20, 1955), No. 18; *Gauguin,* New York, Wildenstein (April 4-May 5, 1956), No. 14, pl. 14, p. 35; *Masterpieces Recalled,* New York, Raul Rosenberg (February 5-March 2, 1957), No. 29, ill. p. 31; *Gauguin,* Chicago, Art Institute (February 12-March 29, 1959), No. 16, pl. p. 28; *Gauguin and the Pont Aven Group,* London, Tate Gallery (January 7-February 13, 1966), Zurich, Kunsthaus (March 5-April 11, 1966); *Paintings from the Albright-Knox Art Gallery,* Washington, D. C., National Gallery of Art (May 18-July 21, 1968).

LITERATURE: *Gallery Notes* (June, 1947), Vol. XI, No. 3, pp. 3-13, ill. p. 2; Maurice Malingue, "Gauguin, le peintre et son oeuvre," *Les presses de la cité* (Paris, and New York, 1948), ill. No. 147; *History of Modern Painting* (Geneva, 1950), Vol. II, pp. 8-9, ill. p. 9; John Rewald, *Paul Gauguin* (New York, 1952), ill. p. 9; *Gauguin* (New York, 1953), ill. p. 46; Henri Dorra, *Paul Gauguin* (New York, 1953); Robert Goldwater, *Paul Gauguin* (New York, 1957), p. 92, ill. p. 93; H. W. Janson with Dora Jane Janson, eds., *Key Monuments of the History of Art, A Visual Survey* (New York, 1959), ill. p. 993; John Rewald, *Paul Gauguin* (New York, 1954), ill. p. 11; Ronald Alley, *Gauguin* (London, 1961), pl. XVI and notes on the plate p. 44; *Gauguin* (Milan, 1964), ill.; Dora Vallier, *Gauguin* (Bergamo, 1965), p. 27, ill.

(BARON) FRANCOIS-PASCAL-SIMON GERARD
Rome, 1770-1837, Paris

Son of a French diplomat in Rome, Gérard arrived in Paris at the age of twelve where he was granted a royal pension for the study of art. He subsequently studied with Pajou for two years and, from 1786, with David. By 1800 his reputation was fully established, and Napoleon in that year entrusted him to carry out portraits of the royal household. Not only did he enjoy the patronage of Napoleon but fared equally well during the Restoration, being made court painter to Louis XVIII in 1817. He is best known as a chronicler of the events and personages of his times, bestowing upon them pictorially the grandeur they felt themselves to represent.

38. MADEMOISELLE DUCHESNOIS DANS LE RÔLE DE DIDON

(Mlle Duchesnois as Dido)
Oil on canvas, 25¾ x 21½
Musée Carnavalet, Paris

EX-COLL: Rothan Collection, Paris, 1890; Doistau Collection; Musée Carnavalet, 1910.

EXHIBITIONS: *Portraits du siècle*, Paris (1883), No. 100; *Exposition universelle*, Paris (1900), No. 127; *Exposition de peinture française*, Rome and Milan (1955); *Exposition Ingres*, Musée de Montauban (1967); *The Taste of Paris*, Atlanta (1968), No. 34.

LITERATURE: Thieme-Becker, "Gérard," *Allgemeines Lexicon der Bildenden Kunstler.*

JEAN-LOUIS-ANDRE-THEODORE GERICAULT

Rouen, 1791-1824, Paris

A pupil of Vernet and later of Guérin, Géricault was further influenced by Gros, particularly in his paintings of horses and his choice of contemporary subjects. Géricault abandoned the use of detailed preparatory drawings and studies, painting directly on the final canvas from models posed according to a painted sketch. As an ardent Bonapartist, Géricault eventually sided with the liberal opponents of the restored Monarchy, an alignment reflected in many of his drawings and particularly in his most celebrated work, *The Raft of the Medusa* (1819). In 1816 he visited Italy for a year, and in 1820-1822 remained in England where his *Raft* was shown in a traveling exhibition. His influence on the development of the Romantic movement was great; and his art, as that of Gros and Rubens, served as special inspiration for the young Delacroix who admired him deeply.

39. LE FOU ASSASSIN, 1822-1823

(The Mad Assassin)
Oil on canvas, 24 x 19⅝
Museum voor Schone Kunsten, Ghent, Belgium

EX-COLL: Dr. Georget; Dr. Lachèze; Charles Jacque; P. A. Cheramy; Sale Cheramy, Paris, May 7, 1908, No. 57.

EXHIBITIONS: *Géricault,* Paris (1924), No. 263; *Chefs-d'oeuvre du musée de Gand,* Brussels, Lille, Luxembourg, Liége (1948), No. 37; *Vingtcinq ans du Palais des Beaux-Arts,* Brussels (1953); *Théodore Géricault,* Winterthur, Kunstmuseum (1953), No. 107, pl. XXIII; *Capovalori dell' ottocento francese,* Rome, Milan (1955), No. 50; *The Romantic Movement,* London, Arts Council (1959), No. 178, pl. 17; *Französische Malerei des 19 Jahrhunderts,* Munich, Haus der Kunst (1964).

LITERATURE: Ch. Clément, *Géricault* (Paris, 1879), No. 157; Louis Rosenthal, *La peinture romantique,* III (Paris, 1900); *Les arts* (1907), No. 64, p. 18; R. Régarney, *Géricault* (Paris, 1926), pl. 27; G. Opresco, *Géricault* (Paris, 1927); M. Gauthier, *Géricault* (Paris, 1935), p. 50; *L'amour de l'art-Prométhée* (Paris, 1939), p. 18, ill.; *Journal of the Warburg and Courtauld Institutes* (1940-1941), Vol. IV, pp. 151-163, pl. 136c; K. Berger, *Géricault und sein Werk* (Vienna, 1952), pp. 58, 79, No. 91, ill.; D. Aime-Azam, *Mazeppa* (Paris, 1956), pp. 231, 344; *The Romantic Movement* (London, 1959).

JEAN-LOUIS-ANDRE-THEODORE GERICAULT

Rouen, 1791-1824, Paris

40. LE RADEAU DE LA MEDUSE (Study), 1818

Oil on canvas, 14¾ x 18⅛

Musé du Louvre, Paris (RF2229)

EX-COLL: Géricault Sale, Paris, 1864, No. 4; Bequest of Baron Schickler, 1919.

EXHIBITIONS: *Géricault*, Paris (1924), No. 135; *Frankst Malerkunst*, Copenhagen, Stockholm and Oslo (1928), No. 77; *Gros, ses amis, ses élèves*, Paris (1936), No. 843; *Franske Kunst*, Copenhagen (1938), No. 56; *Art français*, Belgrade (1939), No. 56; *De David a nuestros dias*, Buenos Aires (1939), No. 64; *Delacroix et les compagnons de sa jeunesse*, Paris, Atelier de Delacroix (1947), No. 40; *Géricault*, Winterthur, Switzerland (1953), No. 77; *Géricault*, Charleroi, France (1962), No. 3; *Delacroix*, Bordeaux (1963), No. 284; *Le Romantisme dans la peinture français*, Moscow-Leningrad (1968-1969), No. 58.

LITERATURE: Ch. Clement, *Géricault* (Paris, 1879), pl. 124, p. 302, No. 98; K. Berger, *Géricault* (Vienna, 1952), p. 70, No. 42, pl. 42; Ch. Sterling and H. Adhémar, *La peinture au musée du Louvre, l'ecole française, le XIXe Siècle* (Paris, 1959), Vol. I, No. 945, pl. 338; N. V. Prokofief. *Théodore Géricault* (Moscow, 1963), ill. pl. 136.

JEAN-LEON GEROME

Vesoul (Haute-Saone), 1824-1904, Paris

Gérome went to Paris in 1841, and the following year became a pupil of Paul Delaroche with whom he went to Italy. *The Cock Fight* won him a medal in the Salon of 1847, and thereafter he was seldom out of favor at the Salon. Gérome travelled widely: to Turkey and the Danube provinces in 1854, and to Egypt in 1857. He married a daughter of the wealthy printer Goupil. In 1865 he was named professor of the Ecole des Beaux-Arts, and in 1878 a Grand Commander of the Legion of Honor. Some of Gérome's most exotic paintings are of Eastern subjects. To these as to his historical and classical subjects he brought his extraordinary draughtsmanship and a flair for dramatic and surface detail. At the end of his life Gérome renounced painting and devoted himself with no less brilliance to sculpture.

41. RÉCEPTION DES AMBASSADEURS SIAMOIS, 1864

(Reception of the Siamese Ambassadors)
Oil on canvas, 47½ x 102½
Unsigned
Musée national de Versailles, Palais de Versailles,
Versailles, France (MV5004)

EXHIBITIONS: Salon, Paris (1865).

ANNE-LOUIS GIRODET DE ROUCY TRIOSON

Montargis, 1767-1824, Paris

As an orphan, Girodet was adopted by his tutor Trioson at an early age; he later became a favorite student of David and in 1789 was awarded the coveted Prix de Rome. His painting, *The Sleep of Endymion*, the great salon success of 1792, clearly reflects a predilection for combining the romantic and the classical. Girodet prospered during the Directoire, receiving an order from the Emperor for a painting of *Ossian Receiving Napoleon's Generals*. In his *Portrait of Mlle. Lange as Danaë*, he borrowed devices of calculated artificiality, elongated proportions, and eroticism from the 16th century mannerists to heighten his vicious satire. After 1808, Girodet drifted from David's classicism towards more poetic and romantic themes, but his works continued to suggest a curious eclecticism. Always able to adapt his style to suit a new regime, Girodet continued to be appreciated during the Restoration; and it was then that the Louvre acquired many of his works.

41a. PORTRAIT OF MLLE. LANGE AS DANAË, 1799

Oil on canvas, 25½ x 21¼
The Minneapolis Institute of Arts

EX-COLL: Henri-Guillaume Chatillon; Raoul Brinquant, Paris; George Ansley, England.

EXHIBITIONS: *Salon*, Paris (1799), No. 148 (withdrawn at the request of the model); *David et ses élèves*, Paris, Petit Palais (1913), No. 135; *Gros: ses amis, ses élèves*, Paris, Petit Palais (1936), No. 316; *The Painting of France Since the French Revolution*, San Francisco, De Young Museum (1940), No. 50; *La Comédie-Française*, Château, Versailles (1962), No. 195.

LITERATURE: P. A. Coupin, *Oeuvres posthumes de Girodet-Trioson* (Paris, 1829), I, pp. XIV-XV, LVII; R. Hénard, "Mlle. Lange en Danaé, *La Liberté* (April 16, 1913); G. Lévitine, "The Influence of Lavater and Girodet's 'Expression des Sentiments de l'Amé," *Art Bulletin* (March, 1954), pp. 38-39, ill.; Musée Montargis, *Girodet* (Montargis, 1967), cited, ill.

GOGH, VINCENT VAN

Zundert, The Netherlands, 1853-1890, Auvers-sur-Oise

A failure at everything he attempted — love, the ministry, teaching, and an intense desire to serve his fellow man — Van Gogh turned in the last ten years of his life to painting. During this short period he made hundreds of drawings and paintings which represent some of the best work produced during the 19th century. Abandoning his Dutch heritage, he became associated with the Impressionists and other progressive painters of Paris. Through these contacts and because of visits to the sunny south of France, his paintings took on a brilliance of color and directness of statement which gave definition to "expressionistic" painting. These works startled and interested his artistic friends but antagonized the common man he was so anxious to reach. In a reoccurring period of deep depression, he took his own life in 1890. His intensely difficult life is documented in a long series of deeply moving letters to his beloved brother Theo.

42. LA MAISON DE LA CRAU, 1888

(Tall House)
Oil on canvas, 24⅝ x 20½
Signed, lower right: Vincent
Albright-Knox Art Gallery, Buffalo

EX-COLL: A. Conger Goodyear, New York.

EXHIBITIONS: *Exhibition*, Amsterdam, Municipal Museum (July-August, 1905), No. 161; *Exhibition*, Cambridge, Massachusetts, Fogg Museum (1929); *A Conger Goodyear Collects*, Buffalo, Albright-Knox Gallery (April 30-June 5, 1966), No. 17; *Paintings from the Albright-Knox Art Gallery*, Washington, D.C., National Gallery of Art (May 18-June 21, 1968).

LITERATURE: *Van Gogh's Letters to His Brother*, de LaFaille, ed. (Paris), Vol. III, letter 535, p. 169, No. 561-F. 550, ill. p. 392; Albright-Knox Gallery, *A. Conger Goodyear Collects* (Buffalo, 1966), p. 6, ill. p. 8.

FRANCOIS-MARIUS GRANET

Aix-en-Provence, 1777-1849, Aix-en-Provence

After receiving preliminary instruction from an unknown itinerant artist, Granet was placed in a free school of art directed by Constantine, an influential landscape painter. Following the seige of Toulan in which he participated, Granet met the young Comte de Forbin whom he visited in Paris in 1797. De Forbin, a pupil of David, persuaded Granet to enter the same studio, but in 1802 he departed for Rome where he remained until 1819. The same year, Louis Philippe decorated Granet with the *Chevalier de l'Orde St. Michel* and appointed him as *Conservateur des Tableaux* at Versailles. He became a member of the Institut de France in 1830, but in spite of these honors and his close friendship with de Forbin, then director of the Louvre, Granet constantly returned to Rome. In 1848 he returned to Aix where he died a year later.

43. PAYSAGE D'ITALIE AVEC FABRIQUES DANS LE LOINTAIN
(before 1824)

(Landscape with Distant Buildings)
Paper laid down on canvas, 8⅜ x 11¼
Musée Granet, Musée des Beaux-Arts, Aix-en-Provence (157.6)

EX-COLL: Bequeathed by Granet, 1849.

EXHIBITIONS: *Paysage français du XVIe siècle au XXe siècle*, London (1949); *Italie de Granet*, Aix-en-Provence, Musée Granet (1962).

JEAN-ANTOINE GROS

Paris, 1771-1835, Paris

As a student of the Neo-Classicist David, Gros fought all his life with his "Classic" training and his "Romantic" predispositions. (He drowned himself in the Seine in 1835). He became Napoleon's official painter, traveling with him on his campaigns. In this capacity he found a temporarily fortuitous combination for the expression of his complex personality and considerable talents. For the heroics of Neo-Classicism he found a perfect subject in his Christ-like treatments of Napoleon. His strong color and his interest in the macabre were ideally suited to the real or imagined color of Napoleon's southern campaign and the exoticism of mosques, Arab chieftains, and North African plague quarters. In the early part of the 19th century he represented the merging of "Classic" and "Romantic." He was to have an important effect upon Delacroix and Géricault.

44. BONAPARTE VISITING THE PEST-RIDDEN OF JAFFA, 1804

Oil on canvas, 65¾ x 46½
Unsigned
Museum of Fine Arts, Boston
Sylvanus A. Denio Fund (47.1059)

EX-COLL: Duc de Trevise, Paris.

EXHIBITIONS: *Gros*, Paris, Petit Palais (1936), No. 29; *Bonaparte in Egypt*, Paris, Musée de l'Orangerie (1938), No. 78; *Gros, Géricault, and Delacroix*, New York, Knoedler's (1938), No. 3, ill.; *Golden Gate International Exposition*, San Francisco, Palace of Fine Arts (1940), No. 273; *From David to Courbet*, Detroit, Institute of Arts (1950), No. 7; *Gros, Painter of Battles, The First Romantic Painter*, Cleveland, Museum of Art and Minneapolis, Institute of Arts (1956); *French Masters, Rococo to Romanticism*, Los Angeles, University of California (1961), ill. p. 32.

LITERATURE: W. Friedländer, *David to Delacroix* (Cambridge, Massachusetts, 1952), pp. 62-63, fig. 34.

PAUL-CAMILLE GUIGOU

Villars, 1834-1871, Paris

Guigou, dead at thirty-seven, painted only about a dozen years. His late start was due to his beginnings as a notary, a profession he was happy to abandon for painting. His artistic studies were carried out at the Ecole des Beaux-Arts at Marseille, but he had established himself in Paris by 1862. Always a provincial at heart, however, he did most of his work in the environs of his birthplace. His landscapes, mostly small, are notable for their directness and honesty of approach, being basically free of the regimens of any particular "school." He attempted to express in paint the joy he felt in his native countryside.

45. LES COLLINES D'ALLAUCH, 1862

(Allouch Landscape)
Oil on canvas, 39¾ x 78¼
Signed and dated, lower right
Musée des Beaux-Arts, Marseille

EX-COLL: Acquired from the artist, 1881.

EXHIBITIONS: *Paul Guigou*, Paris, Musée du Luxembourg (1927), No. 14; *Chefs-d'oeuvre de l'art français*, Paris (1937), No. 123; *Paul Guigou*, Marseille, Musée Cantini (1959), No. 3.

LITERATURE: André Gouirand, *Les peintres provençaux* (Paris, 1901); Théodore Duret, "Un grand peintre de la Provence: Paul Guigou," *L'art et les artistes*, No. 87 (June, 1912); Armand Dayot, "Paul Guigou," *L'art et les artistes* (May, 1927); François Daulte, "Un provençal pur: Paul Guigou," *Connaissance des arts* (April, 1960), ill. p. 75.

JEAN-BAPTISTE-ARMAND GUILLAUMIN
Paris, 1841-1927, Orly

Among the less well-known Impressionist masters, Guillaumin was a sympathetic and perceptive follower rather than an innovator. An early predilection for art led to training at the Académie Suisse and later to close friendships with some of the leading Impressionist painters. The influence of Cézanne, one of his earliest and closest friends, is often detectable in both his composition and technique. However, his use of color was both darker in tonality and, in his later works, more arbitrarily abstract than that of his Impressionist friends. His works thus form an indirect link with those of Gauguin and later Fauve painters of the early 20th century.

46. LE CHEMIN VERS LA VALLÉE (Creuse), 1885

    (The Road to the Valley)
    Oil on canvas, 46⅛ x 35
    Signed and dated, lower right: Guillaumin 85
    Musée du Petit Palais, Paris

EX-COLL: Siegfried Propper, 1917; acquired by the City of Paris, 1917.

EXHIBITIONS: *Quelques oeuvres des collections de la Ville de Paris*, Bern, La Chaux-de-Fonds, Geneva, Basel (1947), No. 43; *Petit Palais, Musée de la Ville de Paris*, Zurich, Kunsthaus (1947), No. 223; *Un siècle de peinture française 1850-1950*, Lisbon, Fondation Calouste Gulbenkian (1965), ill.

HENRI-JOSEPH HARPIGNIES

Valenciennes, 1819-1916, St. Privé

Harpignies, whose first career was that of a commercial traveler, began as a landscape painter after his first trip to Italy in 1850-1852. His first real successes were landscapes done in the province of Nivernais. However, Harpignies never concentrated on any particular region of France, but traveled around the country painting the gently wooded hills, the forests, streams, and grey skies. Harpignies was influenced by Corot and the Barbizon school, but he was largely unaffected by the other movements in French art going on around him and continued to paint in one style all his life. Harpignies' paintings — watercolors as well as oils — reflect his love of nature and his delight in the simple beauties of the countryside.

47. LEVER DE LUNE, LA LOIRE À BRIARE, 1866

(Moonrise on the Loire)
Oil on canvas, 54 x 87¼
Signed and dated, lower left
Lent by Mr. Walter P. Chrysler, Jr., New York

EX-COLL: Bapterosse, Paris; M. Chaulot, Paris, 1954.

EXHIBITIONS: *Salon,* Paris (1885), No.1229; *French Paintings 1789-1929 from the Collection of Walter P. Chrysler, Jr.,* Dayton, Ohio, The Dayton Art Institute (March 25-May 22, 1960), No. 31; *The Controversial Century: 1850-1950,* Provincetown, Massachusetts, Chrysler Art Museum (June 15-September 3, 1962), Ottawa, The National Gallery of Canada (September 27, 1962-November 4, 1962); *French Landscape Painters from Four Centuries,* New York, Finch College Museum of Art (October 20, 1965-January 9, 1966), No. 31.

LITERATURE: L. Enault, *Salon* (Paris, 1885), p. 43; H. Harvard, *Salon* (Paris, 1885), p. 50; The Dayton Art Institute, *French Paintings 1789-1929 from the Collection of Walter P. Chrysler, Jr.,* No. 31, p. 39; Chrysler Art Museum, *The Controversial Century: 1850-1950;* Finch College Museum of Art, *French Landscape Painters from Four Centuries,* No. 31.

JEAN-JACQUES HENNER

Bernviller, 1829-1905, Paris

Henner received his initial art training from the Alsatian painter Gutzwiller. This was followed in 1874 by a formal education at the Ecole des Beaux-Arts under Drolling and Picot. In 1858 he won a Prix de Rome for his painting entitled *Adam et Eve retrouvant le corps d'Abel*. Among other professional distinctions, Henner took a Grand Prix for painting at the Paris International Exhibition in 1900. Henner's work, a combination of realism and idealism reminiscent of Correggio, is notable for its refined use of texture and color. His best-known paintings were of nudes, usually in historical settings; however, like a true 19th-century dilletante, he also excelled at painting landscapes and portraits.

48. MARY MAGDALENE AT THE TOMB OF THE SAVIOR, 1880

Oil on canvas, 48½ x 36¾
Signed and dated, lower right: J. J. Henner 1880
The Toledo Museum of Art, Toledo
Gift of Arthur J. Secor (30.213)

EX-COLL: Sarah M. Hitchcock, 1880-1930.

EXHIBITIONS: *Exhibition*, New York, Metropolitan Museum of Art (on loan 1891-1930); *Exhibitions of Paintings by Old and Modern Masters*, Rhode Island, The Art Association of Newport (1930), No. 20, ill. frontispiece.

LITERATURE: *Metropolitan Museum of Art Catalogue* (1905), No. 566, p. 73; *Art News* (December 6, 1930), XXIX, p. 17, ill.; *Art News* (February 7, 1931), p. 14; *Toledo Museum News* (June, 1931), No. 60, ill.; *Art Digest* (August, 1931), p. 12, ill.; Blake-More Godwin, *European Paintings in the Toledo Museum* (1939), p. 212, ill. p. 213.

PAUL HUET

Paris, 1803-1869, Paris

A brilliant student, Huet appeared destined at first for an academic career rather than one as an artist. A landscapist of great strength and originality, he was trained by pupils of David, notably Guérin (1817-1818). Huet was further influenced by Constable whose works were shown in the Salon of 1824 and were more appreciated by the French than the English. His interest in nature and atmospheric effects placed him in rapport with Rousseau, Dupré, and Diaz, and he was further a life-long friend of both Delacroix and Bonington. His landscapes, done in almost every region of France, are perhaps most properly called "pre-impressionist" rather than "Barbizon." They cannot easily be categorized with any school grouping.

49. LES FALAISES DE HOULGATE, ca. 1862

(View of the Cliffs of Houlgate)
Oil on canvas, 61¾ x 89⅜
Signed, lower right: Paul Huet
Musée des Beaux-Arts, Bordeaux

EX-COLL: Gift of the state in 1863.

EXHIBITIONS: *Salon*, Paris (1863); *Salon*, Paris, Palais des Beaux-Arts (1911), No. 156; *La vie du musée de 1939 à 1947*, Bordeaux, Musée de peinture et de sculpture (1947), No. 133; *Paul Huet*, Rouen, Musée des Beaux-Arts (1965), No. 78; *Le Romantisme dans la peinture française en U.R.S.S.*, Paris, Association Française d'Action Artistique (November 1968-February, 1969).

LITERATURE: E. Vallet, *Catalogue des tableaux, sculptures, gravures, dessins exposés dans les galeries du musée de Bordeaux*, (Bordeaux, 1881), No. 507, p. 167; E. Vallet, *Nouvelle édition du catalogue* (Bordeau, 1894), No. 613, p. 178; D. Alaux, *Musée de peinture de Bordeaux* (Bordeaux, 1910), No. 475, p. 90; Ch. Saunier, *Bordeaux* (Paris, 1925), p. 127; Th. Ricaud, *Musée de peinture et de sculpture de Bordeaux de 1830 à 1870* (Bordeaux, 1938), pp. 147 and 179; P. Miquel, *Paul Huet* (Sceaux, 1962), p. 213; Th. Guedy, *Musée de France* (Paris, n.d.), No. 507, p. 104.

JEAN-AUGUSTE-DOMINIQUE INGRES

Montauban, 1780-1867, Paris

As a student of David, Ingres was thought of as the continuer of the master's Neo-Classicism though, in fact, he claimed a greater devotion to Raphael than to his former teacher. Through an early extended period of study in Florence, he developed an admirable drawing skill and a life-long devotion to draughtsmanship as the predominant element of art. Being a gifted man, of public importance and absolute self-confidence, he was the "classical" force in France in the 19th century. He was the prime opponent of Delacroix and Romanticism. His best works are thought to be his early line portrait drawings and the portrait paintings which he did throughout his life while he personally consistently preferred his large heroic-didactic works. His work and life had a considerable effect upon the artistic development of the 19th century. The discussion of his real contribution continues.

50. ROGER DÉLIVRANT ANGÉLIQUE, 1819

(Roger and Angelica)
Oil on canvas, 57⅞ x 74¾
Signed and dated on the rock: J.A.D. Ingres. P. it. Rome. 1819
Musée du Louvre, Paris (INV. 5419)

EX-COLL: Louis XVIII (Salon de 1819); la Salle du Trône, Versailles; Musée du Luxembourg, 1824; Musée du Louvre, 1874.

EXHIBITIONS: *Salon*, Paris (1819), not catologued; *Exposition universelle*, Paris (1855), No. 3349; *Ingres*, Paris, Ecole des Beaux-Arts (1867), No. 19; *Ingres*, Paris (1967), No. 107; *Ingres in Italia*, Rome (1968), No. 78; *Le Romantisme dans la peinture française*, Moscow-Leningrad (1868-1969), No. 105.

LITERATURE: H. Delaborde, *Ingres, sa vie, ses travaux, sa doctrine* (Paris, 1870), No. 32; J. Mommeja, *Ingres* (Paris, 1904), pp. 62-67, ill. p. 73; H. Lapauze, *Ingres, sa vie et son oeuvre* (Paris, 1911), pp. 194-198 and 475, ill. p. 19L; J. Alazard, *Ingres et l'ingrisme* (Paris, 1950), pp. 70, 72, 100; G. Wildenstein, *Ingres, catalogue complet des peintures* (London, 1954) (French edition), No. 124, pl. 52; Ch. Sterling and H. Adhémar, *La peinture au musée du Louvre, l'école française, le XIXe siecle* (Paris, 1959), Vol. I, No. 1104, pl. 401; R. Rosenblum, *Ingres* (New York, 1967), p. 140; E. Camasasca, *Ingres* (Milan, 1968).

JEAN-AUGUSTE-DOMINIQUE INGRES

Montauban, 1780-1867, Paris

51. MADEMOISELLE JEANNE GONIN*

Oil on fabric, 30 x 23⅞
Taft Museum, Cincinnati (1931.414)

EX-COLL: Pyrame Thomeguex (married Jeanne Gonin, died 1844); Antoine Thomeguex (son, died in 1899); Albert Thomeguex (grandson, died in 1918); Mme. Paul-Gaston Pictet (Alice Thomeguex, sister of Albert); Gallery Scott & Fowles, New York; Charles Phelps Taft, 1924; Taft Museum, 1931.

EXHIBITIONS: *Ingres*, Paris, Ecole des Beaux-Arts (1867); *A Century of Progress Exhibition*, Chicago, Art Institute (1933); *David and Ingres*, Springfield, Massachusetts, Museum of Fine Arts (1939); New York, Knoedler (1940); Cincinnati, Art Museum (1940); *French Painting from David to Courbet*, Detroit, Institute of Fine Arts (1950); *Twentieth Anniversary Exhibition, The Beginnings of Modern Painting, France, 1800-1910*, Omaha, Nebraska, Joslyn Art Museum (1951); *Paintings and Drawings by Ingres from the Ingres Museum at Montauban*, Cincinnati, Art Museum (1953); *Ingres in American Collections*, New York, Paul Rosenberg Gallery (1961); *One Hundredth Anniversary of the Death of J. D. Ingres*, Paris, Petit Palais (1967-1968).

LITERATURE: Edmond Saglio, *Un nouveau tableau de M. Ingres* (Paris, 1857), p. 77; Henri Delabordo, *Ingres* (Paris, 1870), No. 124; Charles Blanc, *Ingres* (Paris, 1870), p. 232; Henry Lapauze, *Les dessins de J.-A.-D. Ingres du musée de Montauban* (Paris, 1901), pp. 235, 248; Henry Lapauze, *Sur un portrait inédit de Ingres:* Mm. *Gonin-Thomeguex, La renaissance de l'art français* (Paris, ca. 1923), p. 446, ill. opp. p. 446; Walter H. Siple, "Two Portraits by Ingres," *Bulletin of the Cincinnati Art Museum* (April, 1930), pp. 35, 37, 39, ill. p. 25; "Ingres in a Little-Known Portrait," *The Connoisseur* (London, 1933), p. 347, ill. p. 348; Walter Pach, *Ingres* (New York/London, 1939), p. 26, ill. opp. p. 111; Jean Alazard, *Ingres et l'ingrisme* (Paris, 1950), p. 66; Georges Wildenstein, *Ingres* (Paris/London, 1954), No. 147, pl. 54; Hans Naef and Louise Burroughs, *Ingres et les familles Gonin*, (Geneva, 1966), Vol. XIV; *Catalogue*, Ingres Exhibition, (Petit Palais), p. 176, ill. 177.

*Exhibited only during July.

CHARLES-EMILE JACQUE

Paris, 1813-1894, Paris

Jacque began his artistic career as an apprentice to a Parisian map-maker, and was later engaged as an illustrator and a graphic artist. He was one of the first painter-etchers of the 19th century. At thirty-two he seriously took up painting and allied himself with the Barbizon School, becoming a close friend of both Millet and Diaz, and was responsible for Millet's move to Barbizon in 1849. As an artist Jacque distinguished himself as a painter of animals, especially sheep and poultry; he also gained recognition as a careful and scientific breeder of chickens. He exhibited only three times at the Salon, in 1861, and again in 1863 and 1864. In 1867 he received the riband of the Legion of Honor, and in 1889 his etching *La Bergerie Béarnaise* earned him the Medal of Honor at the Paris Exposition. He long outlived his Barbizon confreres, and although less talented and original than they, his animal subjects complement their predominantly figural and landscape concerns.

52. LE GRAND TROUPEAU AU PÂTURAGE, 1880

(Shepherd and Flock)
Oil on canvas, 102¼ x 82½
Signed and dated, lower right
Chrysler Art Museum, Provincetown, Massachusetts

EX-COLL: Acquired from the artist's son.

EXHIBITIONS: *Salon*, Paris (1888), No. 1343; *Atelier Jacque*, Paris (1894), No. 1; *French Paintings 1789-1929 from the Collection of Walter P. Chrysler, Jr.*, Dayton, Ohio, The Dayton Art Institute (March 25-May 22, 1960), No. 34.

LITERATURE: H. Houssaye, *Le Salon* (Paris, 1888), p. 72; T. H. Bartlett, "Barbizon," *Scribner's Magazine* (May, 1890), p. 539; *Atelier Jacque* (Paris, 1894), No. 1; The Dayton Art Institute, *French Paintings 1789-1929 from the Collection of Walter P, Chrysler, Jr.*, No. 34, p. 42.

GEORGES LACOMBE
Versailles, 1868-1916, Alençon

Both a painter and sculptor, Lacombe received his earliest instruction from his mother Laure. She was herself an artist who had trained with Raffet. His association with the Nabis at Pont Aven, however, was the formative experience in his career. The influence of the strong patterns and colors of Gauguin and Sérusier is felt in his work, and to this he added a personal symbolism with medieval overtones. He knew and worked with Bertrand, Roussel, Denis, and Bonnard and made portrait busts of all of them for Ranson's marionette theatre. With the outbreak of war in 1914 he abandoned painting to become an orderly and died in 1916 as a result of a fatal illness contracted in service.

53. LA MER JAUNE

(The Yellow Sea)
Oil on canvas, 23⅞ x 32
Signed, lower right center: GL
Musée Municipal, Brest (65-191-1)

EX-COLL: The artist: Mme Mona-Lacombe, Paris.

EXHIBITIONS: *Paul Gauguin et le groupe de PONT-AVEN*, Pont-Aven, Hôtel de Ville (1963), No. 45; *Nabis*, Mannheim, Stadtische Kunsthalle (1963), No. 147; *Exhibition*, Galleria del Levante, Milan (1964), No. 0801.

LITERATURE: Joelle Ansieau, *Georges Lacombe* (Unpublished Thesis) (Paris, 1968).

EDOUARD MANET

Paris, 1832-1883, Paris

Manet studied under the painter Thomas Couture from 1850 until 1856. He reacted strongly against academic painting, and began working in a new style influenced by Spanish painting after 1859. His early technique was based on the use of strong light and shadow with little halftone. Working directly from the model, Manet painted with immediacy, using a restricted palette. He submitted works frequently to the Salon which were, however, often refused, or if admitted, scorned. Among the critics, Baudelaire and Zola were the first to accept his work. Manet played an important part in the Salon des Refusés in 1863 where his famous *Déjeuner sur l'herbe* was shown. From 1870, his work became more impressionistic in color and technique although he did not participate in the Impressionist Exhibitions. He knew Degas, Pissarro, and many of the other Impressionists but was never closely associated with them.

54. LE FUMEUR, 1866

(The Smoker)
Oil on canvas, 39½ x 32
Signed, lower right
The Minneapolis Institute of Arts, Minneapolis
Anonymous Gift of Funds (68.79)

EX-COLL: The artist; M. Pertuiset, 1866; Vente Pertuiset, Paris, 1888, No. 1 (as *La Bonne Pipe – Pendant du Bon Bock*); Isidore Bloch, Paris; Durand-Ruel, Paris; E. F. Milliken, New York, 1902; Durand-Ruel, New York; Mrs. Harry Payne Whitney, New York; Parke-Bernet, New York, 1965 (sale of the collection of Mrs. C. McCulloch Miller, New York); Private Collection, Switzerland, 1968.

EXHIBITIONS: *Exposition particulièr,* Paris (1867), No. 49; *Manet Memorial Exhibition,* Paris, Ecole des Beaux Arts (1884), No. 26; Durand-Ruel Galleries, New York (1885); *Masterpieces of Art,* New York World's Fair (1940), No. 278; *Pictures Collected by Yale Alumni,* New Haven, Connecticut, Yale University (1956), No. 72; *Masterpieces,* New York, Wildenstein (1961), No. 35; *Exhibition,* Wildenstein, Philadelphia and Chicago (1966-67).

LITERATURE: T. Duret, *Histoire d'Édouard Manet et de son oeuvre* (Paris, 1902), No. 61; T. Duret, *Manet and the French Impressionists* (Paris, 1910), Appendix I, No. 61, p. 226, E. Moreau-Nélaton, *Manet raconté par lui-même* (Paris, 1926), Vol. I, pp. 86-88, fig. 88, ill.; P. Jamot and G. Wildenstein, *Manet* (1932), Vol. I, No. 133, p. 133, ill., Vol. II, fig. 112; A. Tabarant, *Manet et ses oeuvres* (Paris, 1947), p. 120, ill. p. 606, No. 122; *Time* (April 28, 1961), ill.

EDOUARD MANET

Paris, 1832-1883, Paris

55. LA BRIOCHE, 1870

Oil on canvas, 25½ x 31⅞
Signed and dated, lower right: Manet 1870
Private Collection, New York

EX-COLL: Jean-Baptiste Faure, Paris; Durand-Ruel, Paris; Carl Neilsen, Oslo; Etienne Bignou, Paris; Durand-Ruel, New York; Leonard Gow, Glasgow; Mrs. A. Chester Beatty,
London.

EXHIBITIONS: *Exposition des oeuvres d'Edouard Manet*, Paris, Ecole National des Beaux-
Arts (June 5-28, 1884), No. 85; *La collection Faure*, Paris, Galerie Durand-Ruel (March 1-31,
1906), No. 12; Berlin, Galerie Paul Cassirer; London, Sulley & Company (June 11-30, 1906),
No. 10; *Franco-British Exhibition*, London (1908), No. 331; *Edouard Manet*, Copenhagen,
Ny Karlsberg Glyptotek (January 27-February 17, 1922), No. 15; *Exhibition of French Art:
1200-1900*, London, Royal Academy of Arts, Burlington House (January 4-March 12, 1932),
No. 395; *Manet: 1832-1883*, Paris, Musée de l'Orangerie (June 16-October 9, 1932), No. 43;
L'Impressionisme, Brussels, Palais des Beaux-Arts (June 15-September 29, 1935), No. 35;
Paintings from Private Collections, New York, Museum of Modern Art (May-September,
1955), No. 79; *Works of Art from the Collections of the Class of 1936*, Cambridge, Massa-
chusetts, Fogg Art Museum (June 1-August 25, 1961), No. 16; *Edouard Manet*, Philadelphia,
Museum of Art (November 3-December 11, 1966), and Chicago, Art Institute (January 13-
February 19, 1967), No. 102.

LITERATURE: T. Duret, *Histoire d'Edouard Manet et de son oeuvre* (Paris, 1902), No. 223;
Paul Jamot & Georges Wildenstein, *Manet* (Paris, 1932), No. 181; E. Moreau-Nélaton, *Manu-
script of catalogue of Manet's oeuvre* (Paris, 1906), No. 219; Adolphe Tabarant, *Manet:
Histoire catalographique* (Paris, 1931), No. 154, and *Manet et ses oeuvres* (Paris, 1947).

JEAN-LOUIS-ERNST MEISSONIER

Lyons, 1815-1891, Paris

Judged an artistic giant in his own day, Meissonier is another of those artists whose works until recently have not been appreciated by modern taste. His importance for his contemporaries was largely based upon his abilities as a history painter; yet Meissonier was probably at his best as a painter of genre. As such he exerted a considerable influence on Daumier. Early training at the atelier Cogniet, followed by study in Rome, did not modify his serious desire to emulate the little Dutch masters. His election by acclamation in 1889 as president of the international jury of the Beaux-Arts underlines the prestige which was his during his lifetime. Superlative craftsmanship coupled with enormous facility helped him produce technically excellent works which today can again be appreciated for their considerable merit.

56. LE SIÈGE DE PARIS, 1870-1871

(The Siege of Paris)
Oil on canvas, 21⅛ x 27¾
Signed and dated, lower right (in crayon): 70. E. Meissonier
Musée du Louvre, Paris (RF.1249)

EX-COLL: Mme E. Meissonier.

EXHIBITIONS: *Jean-Louis-Ernest Meissonier*, Paris, Ecole des Beaux-Arts (1893), No. 9; *Manifeste en "Hommage à Meissonier,"* Paris, Hôtel Meurice (November, 1967); *Le Salon imaginaire*, Berlin, Akademie der Kunst (October, 1968), No. 118, ill. p. 71.

LITERATURE: Cte Henri Delaborde, "Notice sur la vie et les ouvrages de Meissonier," Institut de France, Académie des Beaux-Arts (Paris, 1892); pp. 15-16; Henri Roujon, *Meissonier* (Paris, n.d.), Vol. 25, p. 68; L. Bénédite, *Meissonier* (Paris: Coll. Les Grands Artistes), Vol. 33, pp. 69-79; M. O. Greard, *Jean-Louis-Ernest Meissonier, ses souvenirs, ses entretiens* (Paris, 1897), pp. 106, 108, 109. p. 404 (1871), and p. 411 (1884); G. Brière, *Musée national du Louvre — Catalogue des peintures exposées dans les galeries, l'école française* (Paris, 1924), I, No. 2969; Ch. Sterling and H. Adhémar, *La peinture au musée du Louvre, l'école française, le XIXe siècle* (Paris, 1961), Vol. III, No. 1249, pl. 466.

GEORGES MICHEL

Paris, 1763-1843, Paris

The son of a modest working man, Georges Michel was born and died poor. His early training was received in the studio of the painter Leduc and from 1786 to 1814 he exhibited in the Salons, but without selling much as a consequence. From time to time he did works in collaboration with Nicolas Antoine Taunay, who painted the figures. Nonetheless, Michel may be regarded as one of the founders of modern landscape painting and surely the first French Romantic landscape artist. He rejected as anecdotal and inconsequential the decorative landscape style of the late 18th century. Instead, Michel's paintings recall Ruysdael and the 17th-century Dutch landscapists. The main source of his inspiration, however, was the environs of Paris where he rendered the tense, dramatic, and romantic implications of nature.

57. GATHERING STORM

Oil on canvas, 16⅝ x 28⅝
The George A. Lucas Collection, Maryland Institute
Courtesy of The Walters Art Gallery, Baltimore (1991)

EX-COLL: George A. Lucas

EXHIBITIONS: *Exhibition of the George A. Lucas Art Collection*, Baltimore, Maryland Institute (1911), No. 15; *From Ingres to Gauguin*, Baltimore, Museum of Art (1951), No. 2; *The George A. Lucas Collection of The Maryland Institute*, Baltimore, Museum of Art (1965), No. 199.

JEAN-FRANCOIS MILLET

Gruchy, 1814-1875, Barbizon

The son of Norman peasants, Millet had his first professional training in Cherbourg, then moved to Paris where he studied with Paul Delaroche. He had a portrait accepted in the Salon of 1840, but did not have any real success until about 1848. By 1850 Millet had moved with his family to Barbizon where he responded to the rural environment to such an extent that thereafter he rarely painted any other subject. Millet became intimate friends with Théodore Rousseau and under his influence devoted himself to landscape painting. Gradually he became more and more acceptable to the public so that in 1868 he was awarded the Legion of Honor. Robert Herbert points out that although Millet has been almost derided for his Biblical spirit, he was, in reality, a life-long agnostic.

58. MLLE. ONO, ca. 1841

Oil on canvas, 28¾ x 23⅝
Musée Thomas Henry, Cherbourg

EX-COLL: Musée des Beaux-Arts, Cherbourg.

EXHIBITIONS: *French Painting of the 19th Century: From David to Cézanne,* Munich, Haus der Kunst (1964-1965), No. 179, p. 392, ill.

LITERATURE: J. Vergnet-Ruiz and M. Laclotte, *Great French Paintings from the Regional Museums of France* (New York, 1965), pp. 141, 149, No. 164, ill.

34

CLAUDE MONET
Paris, 1840-1926, Giverny

Monet's early years were spent at Le Havre where he was a friend of Eugène Boudin. He went to Paris in 1859 to the Académie Suisse and, following two years of military service, he returned to France in 1862 and joined the atelier of Charles Gleyre where he met Renoir, Sisley, and Bazille. For the next two years he painted in different parts of the French countryside, usually with such artists as Daubigny, Courbet, and Whistler. His work of this period suggests Manet whom he greatly admired. In 1871, after a trip to London, Monet settled at Argenteuil, and three years later promoted the famous 1874 group exhibition in Paris where he and the other exhibitors earned the name "impressionists." During the next decade Monet produced his famous series of paintings which deal with light and the visual effects caused by its daily and seasonal changes. The year 1899 presumably marks the first time he painted water-lilies, a subject which was to occupy him almost exclusively until his death.

59. JARDIN EN FLEURS, 1866-1868

(Flower Garden)
Oil on canvas, 25½ x 21¼
Signed, lower left: Claude Monet
Jeu de Paume, Palais du Louvre, Paris

EX-COLL: Musée du Louvre, 1910.

LITERATURE: Ch. Sterling and H. Adhémar, *La Peinture au musée du Louvre, l'école française, le XIXe Siècle* (Paris, 1960) III, p. 26, No. 1349, ill. pl. 501.

CLAUDE MONET

Paris, 1840-1926, Giverny

60. OLD ST. LAZARE STATION, PARIS, 1877

Oil on canvas, 23½ x 31½
Signed and dated, lower left: Claude Monet 77
The Art Institute of Chicago, Chicago
Mr. and Mrs. Martin A. Ryerson Collection

EX-COLL: Jean Bernheim, Paris; Durand-Ruel, New York, December, 1911; Martin A. Ryerson Collection, 1913.

EXHIBITIONS: *La 3e exposition de peinture*, Paris (April, 1877); *A Century of Progress Exhibition*, Chicago, Art Institute (1933), No. 299; *A Century of Progress Exhibition*, Chicago, Art Institute (1934), No. 219; *European and American Paintings, 1500-1900*, New York World's Fair (May-October, 1940), No. 322; *Diamond Jubilee Exhibition, Masterpieces of Painting*, Philadelphia, Museum of Art (November, 1950-February, 1951), No. 70, ill.; *De David à Toulouse-Lautrec, chefs d'oeuvre des collections américaines*, Paris, Musée de l'Orangerie (April 20 through July, 1955), No. 42, ill. pl. 41; *From David to Cézanne*, Munich, Haus der Kunst (October to December, 1964).

LITERATURE: G. Geffroy, *Claude Monet* (1922), p. 136; *Bulletin of The Art Institute of Chicago* (1925), Vol. 19, p. 19; F. Fels, *Claude Monet* (1922), p. 136; *Bulletin of the Art Institute of Chicago* (1933), Vol. 27, p. 11; H. Tietze, *Meisterwerke Europaeischer Malerei in Amerika* (1935), pl. 289; H. Huth, *Gazette des Beaux-Arts* (April, 1946), Vol. 29, pp. 225-52; Kenneth Clarke, *Landscape into Art* (1949), p. 102; L. Venturi, *Impressionists and Symbolists* (London, 1950), ill. fig. 56.

CLAUDE MONET

Paris, 1840-1926, Giverny

61. LES PEUPLIERS AU BORD DE L'EPTE, 1891

(Poplars)
Oil on canvas, 39½ x 25¾
Signed and dated, lower right
Lent by Mr. and Mrs. David T. Schiff, New York

EX-COLL: Durand-Ruel, Paris; Collection Embericos, United States.

EXHIBITIONS: *Exposition d'art moderne*, Paris, Galerie Manzi-Joyant (1912), No. 145; *Claude Monet*, Paris, Galerie Durand-Ruel (March 2-21, 1914), No. 2; *Claude Monet*, Paris, Galerie Georges Petit (January 4-18, 1924), No. 33; *Paysages par Monet, Pissarro, Renoir, et Sisley*, Paris, Galerie Durand-Ruel (January 14-31, 1933), No. 9; *A Treasury of French Arts*, New York, Wildenstein (Summer, 1964), No. 55; *Olympia's Progeny*, (Fall, 1965), No. 55: *Summer Loan Exhibition*, New York, Metropolitan Museum of Art (Summer, 1967), No. 64; *Summer Loan Exhibition*, New York, Metropolitan Museum of Art (Summer, 1968), No. 122.

LITERATURE: George Besson, *Claude Monet* (Collection des Maîtres, n.d.), p. 50; Raymond Koechlin, "Claude Monet," *Art et Decoration* (February, 1927), p. 43.

GUSTAVE MOREAU

Paris, 1826-1898, Paris

At an early age, Gustave Moreau was sent to study at the Ecole des Beaux Arts under Picot, a highly respected teacher. He first exhibited at the Salon in 1852, but it was his controversial *Oedipus and the Sphinx*, completed in 1864, which marked the beginning of his strongest period characterized by subjects selected from history, religion, and legend. Moreau was the founder of the Symbolist movement, and his works reflect the influence of Chassériau whom he greatly admired. With a determined imagination, Moreau managed to combine a free, impressionistic style with symbolic, allegorical, and literary references. His inexplicable abstractions and preoccupation with the theatrical resulted in works often suggesting bizarre dreams rather than the comfortable pastorals of his contemporaries. Moreau bequeathed some 8,000 works and his Paris home to the state. This later became the Musée National Gustave Moreau.

62. HERCULE ET L'HYDRE DE LERNE, 1876
    (Hercules and the Hydra)
    Oil on canvas, 69 x 60½
    The Art Institute of Chicago, Chicago, Gift of Mrs. Morton Zurcher

EX-COLL: Louis Mante, Marseille.

EXHIBITIONS: *Salon*, Paris (1876), No. 1505; *Exposition universelle*, Paris (1878), Groupe I, Classe I, No. 656; *Gustave Moreau*, Paris, Galerie Georges Petit (1906), No. 75; *Profiles and Perspectives in 19th-Century French Art*, Lawrence, University of Kansas (January 14-February 26, 1958), No. 18.

LITERATURE: Albert Merat, *Le petit salon* (Paris, 1876), p. 18; Victor de Swarte, *Lettres sur le salon de 1876* (Paris, 1876), p. 79; Georges Dufour, *Le grand art et le petit art au salon de 1876* (Amiens, 1876), p. 24; Mario Proth, *Voyage au pays des peintres — salon 1876* (Paris, 1876), p. 123; Emile Bergérat, *Les chefs d'oeuvre d'art à l'exposition universelle de 1878* (Paris, 1878), p. 127; Paul Mantz, *L'art moderne à l'exposition universelle de 1878*, ed. L. Gonse (Paris, 1879), p. 31; Mario Proth, *Les artistes français à l'exposition universelle de 1878*, p. 56; Ary Renan, *Gustave Moreau* (Paris, 1900), pp. 88ff, ill. p. 89; Gustave Larrouemet, *Notice historique sur Gustave Moreau*, Institut de France (Paris, 1901), pp. 15, 59; *L'oeuvre de Gustave Moreau*, with an intro. by G. Desvallières, Musée National Gustave Moreau (Paris, 1906), ill. No. 12; Léon Desnairs, *Gustave Moreau* (Paris, 1913), pp. 67-68, ill. pl. XXVI.

BERTHE-MARIE-PAULINE MORISOT

Bourges, 1841-1895, Paris

A distant relative of Fragonard, Berthe Morisot met Manet at the Louvre in 1860. They developed a lasting relationship in which she was Manet's model, student, and finally relative, for she married the artist's brother Eugène in 1874. Through Manet she met the other Impressionists and her style, originally closer to Corot and Puvis de Chavannes, developed new directions as a result of her association with them. Besides Manet's, Renoir's influence was notable upon her work. Her hallmark is tranquility and femininity and, like her colleagues, a sense of the out-of-doors.

63. MLLE. PONTILLON, 1873

(The Artist's Sister)
Oil on canvas, 17¾ x 28½
Signed, lower right: Berthe Morisot
The Cleveland Museum of Art, Cleveland
Gift of the Hanna Fund

EX-COLL: Gabriel Thomas, Paris; Captain Edward H. Molyneux, Paris; Cesar de Hauke.

EXHIBITIONS: *Exposition d'oeuvres de Berthe Morisot*, Paris, Bernheim-Jeune (1919), No. 3; *Exposition d'oeuvres de Berthe Morisot du cercle de la renaissance*, Paris, Bernheim-Jeune (1929), No. 80, pl. 16; *French Painting 1800-1900*, Pittsburgh, Carnegie Institute (1951), No. 107, ill.; *Quatre siècles d'art français — hommage à la femme*, Brussels, Palais des Beaux-Arts (1953); *De David à Toulouse-Lautrec: chefs-d'oeuvre des collections américaines*, Paris, Musée de l'Orangerie (1955), No. 43, ill. pl. 45; *Paintings, Drawings and Graphic Works by Manet, Degas, Berthe Morisot and Mary Cassatt*, Baltimore, Museum of Art (1962), No. 81, p. 57, fig. 81, p. 35.

LITERATURE: A. Fourreau, *Berthe Morisot* (Paris and London, 1925), p. 39, pl. 4; M. L. Bataille and Georges Wildenstein, *Berthe Morisot* (Paris, 1961), No. 14, pl. 24, ill. pl. 16 as *L'Ombrelle Verte* (dates it 1867); John Rewald, *The History of Impressionism* (New York, 1961), ill. in color, p. 325; *Cleveland Museum of Art Bulletin* (December, 1950), Vol. 37, pp. 205-211, ill. in color, pp. 207-210.

CAMILLE PISSARRO

Saint Thomas, 1830-1903, Paris

In 1870 Monet and Pissarro fled to London to escape the Prussian occupation, and there found Daubigny who introduced them to Durand-Ruel, the accepted art dealer of the Impressionists. In England Pissarro studied the works of Turner and Constable; later he returned to France to settle in Pontoise, where Cézanne came to work with him (1872-1874). In 1874 he countered the Salon's systematic refusal to hang Impressionist works by organizing the first independent picture exhibition in which the word "impressionist" was also first used. It was largely through Pissarro's efforts, especially his gift for reconciling adverse factions, that the Impressionists remained together.

64. GREAT BRIDGE, ROUEN, 1896

Oil on canvas, 28¾ x 36¼
Signed and dated, lower left: C. Pissarro.96
Staatliche Kunsthalle, Karlsruhe

EX-COLL: Dr. Francisco Llobet, Buenos-Aires.

EXHIBITIONS: *Camille Pissarro,* Paris, Galerie Durand-Ruel (1904), No. 95; *Exhibition,* Paris, Galerie Eugène Blot (1907), No. 13; *Internationale Kunstausstellung,* Bremen, Kunsthalle (1910), No. 262; *Rétrospective des oeuvres de Camille Pissarro,* Paris, Galerie Manzi et Joyant (1914), No. 14; *Premier salon de la société des arts de Buenos-Aires,* Buenos Aires (1924), No. 7, ill.; *Amis des arts,* Buenos-Aires (1932), No. 44; *Französiche Malerei des 19 Jahrhunderts von David bis Cézanne,* Munich, Haus der Kunst (1965), No. 206, ill.

LITERATURE: *La Prensa* (Buenos-Aires, January 3, 1931), ill.; C. Mauclair, *Une belle collection argentine des maîtres français du XIXe siècle* (Paris, 1931); *Catalogue de la collection Llobet* (Buenos-Aires, 1932), No. 13; L. R. Pissarro and L. Venturi, *Camille Pissarro: son art–son oeuvre* (Paris, 1939), Vol. I, p. 213, No. 950, Vol. II, pl. 192, ill. p. 950; *Französiche Meister aus der Staatlichen Kunsthalle Karlsruhe* (Karlsruhe, 1963), No. 39, ill.; *La Chronique des Arts,* Supplément, *Gazette des Beaux-Arts* (February, 1964), No. 1164, p. 24, ill. No. 79; J. Lauts, "Erwerbungsbericht Staatliche Kunsthalle Karlsruhe 1952-1963," *Jahrbuch der Staatlichen Kunstsammlungen in Baden-Württemberg I,* (1964), pp. 31ff, note 26, p. 41.

PIERRE-PAUL PRUD'HON

Cluny, 1758-1823, Paris

An early propensity for painting led Prud'hon to study at the Academy of Dijon where he was later apprenticed to François Devosge. Aristocratic patronage supported his move to Paris in 1780; however, a provincial background impeded his early recognition there. Three years of study in Rome subsequently followed. Here study of the Renaissance masters, Raphael, Coreggio, and Leonardo, counteracted the pervasive Neo-Classicism of Canova and David and helped him form his own personal style. In his works the strains of a later Romanticism are freely mixed with a Neo-Classical attention to subject matter. A return to revolutionary Paris brought him not immediate, but belated success. He is above all known for his allegories in which the rational, intellectual, and sometimes dessicated concerns of 18th-century philosophy are warmly presented in an animated and gracious manner.

65. L'UNION DE L'AMOUR ET DE L'AMITIÉ, ca. 1793

(The Union of Love and Friendship)
Oil on canvas, 57½ x 44½
The Minneapolis Institute of Arts, Minneapolis,
William Hood Dunwoody and John R. Van Derlip Funds (64.50)

EX-COLL: Saint-Marc Didot; Mme. Abel Vautier; Duc de Morny, 1863; Baron de Seillière, 1865; Albert de Rothschild; Baron Louis de Rothschild, Vienna; Wildenstein, New York.

EXHIBITIONS: *Salon*, Paris (1793), No. 679, supplement; *Masterpieces of Painting Through Six Centuries*, Brussels, Palais des Beaux Arts (1953), No. 46; *Prud'hon*, Paris, Musée Jacquemart André (1958), No. 2; *Prud'hon*, Dijon, Musée des Beaux Arts (1959), No. 18; *Neo-Classicism: Style and Motif*, Cleveland, Museum of Art (1964), No. 109; *France in the Eighteenth Century*, London, Royal Academy (1968), No. 575.

LITERATURE: Charles Blanc, *Histoire III* (Paris, 1863), p. 22; E. de Goncourt, *Catalogue raisonné . . .* (Paris, 1876), No. 56; Pierre Gauthiez, *Prud'hon* (Paris, 1886), p. 58; Jean Guiffrey, *L'Oeuvre de P.P. Prud'hon* (Paris, 1924), No. 27, pp. 14-16; Étienne Bricon, *Prud'hon* (n.d.), pp. 55-56; A. Brookner, "Prud'hon, Union of Love and Friendship," *Art News* (November, 1960); S. Sachs II, "Prud'hon's *L'Union de l'Amour et de l'Amitié*: A Neo-Classical Allegory," *The Minneapolis Institute of Arts Bulletin* (1965), LIV, pp. 4-18, frontispiece in color.

PIERRE PUVIS DE CHAVANNES

Lyons, 1824-1898, Paris

Born of an aristocratic family, Puvis attended the Ecole Polytechnique, and became a pupil of Henri Sheffer in 1847. After a difficult tenure, he toured Italy for two years, discovering the frescoes of the Italian primitives. Returning to Paris, Puvis frequented the studios of Couture, Delacroix, and Chassériau. In 1850 when he was twenty-six, Puvis successfully submitted his *Pietà* to the Salon, but it was not until the Salon of 1861 that he received great acclaim. Puvis was enormously popular and successful during his own lifetime; in the 1880s literary symbolism created a favorable environment for his art. He was particularly admired by the Symbolists and other post-Impressionist artists who drew from his attempt to create tranquil, poetical allegories reminiscent of monumental Italian frescoes. Puvis' work is characterized by rhythms of serene gestures and an economy of natural detail locked by lines in simple flat areas of color.

66. LE PAUVRE PÊCHEUR, 1881

(The Poor Fisherman)
Oil on canvas, 61 x 75¾
Signed and dated, lower right: Puvis de Chavannes, 1881
Musée du Louvre, Paris (R.F. 506)

EX-COLL: Musée du Luxembourg.

EXHIBITIONS: *Salon*, Paris (1881), No. 1944; *French Art: 1200-1900*, London, Royal Academy (1932), No. 901; *Puvis de Chavannes et la peinture lyonnaise du XIXième siècle*, Musée de Lyon (1937), No. 25; *Eugène Carrière et le symbolisme*, Paris, Musée de l'Orangerie (1949-1950), No. 91; *Puvis de Chavannes*, Paris, Musée Galliéra (1952); *Gustave Geffroy et l'art moderne*, Paris, Bibliothèque nationale (1957); *Die Nabis und ihre Freunde*, Mannheim, Kunsthalle (1963-1964), No. 168; *Secession Europäische Kunst um die Jahrhundertwende*, Munich, Haus der Kunst (1964), No. 459.

LITERATURE: L. Bénédite, *Le Musée du Luxembourg. Les peintures, École française* (Paris, 1924), No. 467, ill. pl. 41; M. Denis, "Définition du Néo-traditionnisme," *Art et critique* (August 23-30, 1890); M. Vachon, *Puvis de Chavannes* (Paris, 1895), pp. 72-73, ill. p. 71; R. Jean, *Puvis de Chavannes* (Paris, 1914), p. 152, ill. pl. XXIII; L. Werth, *Puvis de Chavannes* (Paris, 1926), pp. 10, 27, 28; C. Mauclair, *Puvis de Chavannes* (Paris, 1928), p. 116; R. Goldwater, "Puvis de Chavannes: Some Reasons for a Reputation," *The Art Bulletin* (March, 1946), pp. 33, 39, 40, 42; Ch. Sterling and H. Adhémar, *La peinture au musée national du Louvre, l'école française, le XIXe siècle*, IV (Paris, 1961), No. 1531, ill. pl. 593.

AUGUSTE-FRANCOIS RAVIER

Lyons, 1814-1895, Morestel

Ravier went to Paris to study law but found himself spending more time in the Louvre than in the library. By 1840 he had abandoned his earlier career and taken up art to the extent that he travelled to Italy in the company of Corot and Daubigny. The style he developed, however, while owing something to others, was basically original and independent. He shared with the Impressionists a fascination with the changing effects of light but whereas their interest was objective, Ravier's was nearly religious. He retired to Crémieu in 1855 to live alone and commune with nature, painting the fleeting beauty of light and landscape in his uniquely open fashion.

67. VUE PANORAMIQUE DE CRÉMIEU
 (View of Crémieu)
 Oil on canvas, 27 x 34¼
 Signed lower right
 Lent by Mr. Walter P. Chrysler, Jr., New York

EX-COLL: Bertrand, Paris; Georges Maratier, Paris.

EXHIBITIONS: *French Paintings 1789-1929 from the Collection of Walter P. Chrysler, Jr.*, Dayton, Ohio, The Dayton Art Institute (March 25-May 22, 1960), No. 32.

LITERATURE: The Dayton Art Institute, *French Paintings 1789-1929 from the Collection of Walter P. Chrysler, Jr.*, No. 32, p. 141.

ODILON REDON

Bordeaux, 1840-1916, Paris

A lonely child, Redon's early years were filled with imaginings rather than happenings. At fifteen he began to take drawing lessons from a local artist who encouraged him to study Delacroix and Corot, never to draw a line except in response to his own sensitivity, and to study literature and music. Drafted and wounded during the Franco-Prussian war, Redon returned to his home near Bordeaux to draw the strange images of his elaborate fantasies, images which Redon insisted were based on nature. All of Redon's works have a certain literary character which made them attractive to the Symbolist authors and to Baudelaire. The praise of these writers attracted some attention to Redon, but strangely enough his most successful exhibition was the American Armory show where, because of the interest of Walter Kuhn, Redon received a larger representation and sold more works than any other exhibitor.

68. PORTRAIT DE MME. ODILON REDON, 1882

Oil on canvas, 17¾ x 14½
Signed and dated, lower left: Redon 1882
Jeu de Paume, Musée du Louvre, Paris

EX-COLL: Gift of Mme. Goekoop de Jong to the Luxembourg Museum, 1904; Musée du Louvre, 1929.

EXHIBITIONS: *Art Français*, Berne (1946); *Exhibition*, Berne, Kunsthalle (1858), No. 143; *Odilon Redon, Gustave Moreau, Rodolphe Bresdin*, New York, Museum of Modern Art (1961-1962), Chicago, Art Institute (1962).

LITERATURE: André Mellerio, *Odilon Redon, peintre, dessinateur et graveur* (Paris, 1923); *L'inventaire république française*, No. 1554, pl. 602; K. Berger, *Odilon Redon, Fantasy and Color* (New York, 1965), catalogued p. 195.

ODILON REDON

Bordeaux, 1840-1916, Paris

69. APOLLO, ca. 1905

Oil on canvas, 28¾ x 21⅜
Signed on the lower left: Odilon Redon
Yale University Art Gallery, New Haven
The Philip L. Goodwin Collection, 1907 (1958.20)

EX-COLL: John Quinn, New York; Brummer Gallery, New York; Philip L. Goodwin, New York, 1926.

EXHIBITIONS: *Loan Exhibition of Impressionist and Post-Impressionist Paintings*, New York, Metropolitan Museum (1921), No. 91, p. 21, ill.; *Twentieth Anniversary Exhibition*, Cleveland, Museum of Art (1936), No. 340, p. 127; *French Paintings of the Latter Half of the Nineteenth Century from the Collections of Alumni and Friends of Yale*, New Haven, Yale University Art Gallery (1950), No. 14; *Paintings and Pastels by Odilon Redon*, New York, Paul Rosenberg (1959), No. 15, ill.

LITERATURE: M. W. Watson, "O. Redon, A Great French Lyricist," *The Arts* (February, 1922), Vol. II, pl. p. 274; *The John Quinn Collection of Paintings, Water Colors, Drawings and Sculpture* (New York, 1926), p. 14, pl. p. 105; R. Bacou, *Odilon Redon* (Geneva, 1956), Vol. I, p. 161, footnote 1; "Recent Gifts and Purchases," *Yale University Art Gallery Bulletin* (1959), Vol. XXIV, No. 3 and Vol. XXV, No. 1, ill.

(BARON) JEAN-BAPTISTE REGNAULT

Paris, 1754-1829, Paris

The young Regnault spent his boyhood in the American colonies where his father had come in search of a new life and new fortunes. When these hopes failed to materialize and his father died, Regnault returned to France in 1769. There he studied with Jean Bardin and Michel N. B. Lepicié. He participated in the Salons between 1783 and 1809. Regnault was a contemporary and the rival of another of Bardin's outstanding pupils, Jacques-Louis David. His Neo-Classical style was less strict and heroic than David's, and tended more toward a softened, sensuous interpretation of the classical ideal which resulted in works of a more decorative character. Although like David he was a member of the Institute, his work has never enjoyed the same reputation as that of his competitor.

70. LA TOILETTE DE VÉNUS, 1815

(The Bath of Venus)
Oil on canvas, 97¼ x 80¾
Signed and dated, lower right
Lent by Mr. Walter P. Chrysler, Jr., New York

EX-COLL: Seligman, Paris; William Randolph Hearst; Dr. Siegfried Aram, New York.

EXHIBITIONS: *French Paintings 1789-1929 from the Collection of Walter P. Chrysler, Jr.*, Dayton, Ohio, The Dayton Art Institute (March 25-May 22, 1960), No. 5.

LITERATURE: *Catalogue des tableaux, esquisses, dessins et croquis de M. le Baron Regnault*, vente de l'atelier (Paris, March, 1830), No. 20, p. 14; *French Paintings, 1789-1929 from the Collection of Walter P. Chrysler, Jr.* (Dayton, Ohio, 1960), No. 5, p. 141.

PIERRE-AUGUSTE RENOIR
Limoges, 1841-1919, Cagnes

Renoir began his career as a porcelain painter at the age of thirteen, later entering the studio of Gleyre where he encountered Bazille, Monet, and Sisley. The earliest influence on Renoir came from Diaz whom he met while painting in the Fontainebleau forest, but this was supplanted by the more powerful styles of Courbet, Manet, and Ingres. His subsequent close association with the Impressionists strongly developed his attachment to color and light rather than form, but Renoir's fame rests nonetheless on his paintings of nudes and portraits. The general softness of his style with his ability to gain monumentality while obscuring sharp outlines makes Renoir one of the formidable masters of French art. Upon the death of his close friend Caillebotte, Renoir was named executor of his estate and was responsible for causing Caillebotte's gift of paintings to be accepted by the state.

71. THREE BATHERS, 1897
Oil on canvas, 21½ x 25⅞
Signed, lower right: Renoir
The Cleveland Museum of Art, Cleveland
Purchase from the J. H. Wade Fund (39.269)

EX-COLL: Galerie Bernheim-Jeune, Paris, 1920; Ralph M. Coe, Cleveland, 1920.

EXHIBITIONS: *French Paintings of the late Nineteenth Century*, Cleveland (1921); *Paintings by Manet and Renoir*, Philadelphia, Pennsylvania Museum (1933), p. 19; *Renoir, a Special Exhibition of his Paintings*, New York, Metropolitan Museum of Art (1937), No. 56, pl. 56; *Masterpieces of Art*, New York World's Fair (1940), No. 331; *Renoir Centennial Loan Exhibition*, New York, Duveen Galleries (1941), No. 64, pl. 64; *Loan Exhibition of Masterpieces of Delacroix and Renoir*, New York, Paul Rosenberg (1948), No. 24, ill. p. 73.

LITERATURE: Josephine L. Allen, "Paintings by Renoir," *Bulletin of the Metropolitan Museum of Art* (June, 1937), XXXII, ill. p. 113; Julius Meier-Graefe, *Renoir* (Leipzig, 1929), p. 264, pl. 255; Henry S. Francis, "Renoir's Three Bathers," *Cleveland Museum of Art Bulletin* (February, 1940), XXVII, pp. 17-18, ill. p. 14; Denis Rouart, *Renoir* (Geneva, 1954), ill. in color p. 88; Bruno F. Schneider, *Renoir* (New York, 1958), ill. in color.

PIERRE-AUGUSTE RENOIR

Limoges, 1841-1919, Cagnes

72. LES FILLES DE DURAND-RUEL, 1882

(The Daughters of Durand-Ruel)
Oil on canvas, 32 x 25¾
Signed and dated, lower right: Renoir 82
Lent by Mr. Walter P. Chrysler, Jr., New York

EX-COLL: Paul M. J. Durand-Ruel, Paris, 1882-1921; André F. Aude, Paris; Wildenstein, New York, 1944; Mrs. Byron C. Foy, New York, 1944-1957; Estate of Thelma Chrysler Foy, 1957-1959.

EXHIBITIONS: *Renoir*, New York, Wildenstein (1951), No. 41; *Renoir*, New York, Wildenstein (1958), No. 40; *Special Exhibition*, Provincetown, Chrysler Art Museum (1959); *French Paintings 1789-1929 from the Collection of Walter P. Chrysler, Jr.*, Dayton, Ohio, The Dayton Art Institute (March 25-May 22, 1960), No. 63; *The Controversial Century: 1850-1950*, Provincetown, Chrysler Art Museum (September 3-27, 1962) and The National Gallery of Canada, Ottawa (September 27-November 4, 1962); *Four Masters of Impressionism*, New York, Acquavella Galleries (October 25-November 30, 1968), No. 32.

LITERATURE: A. Vollard, *Renoir: An Intimate Record* (New York, 1934); Wildenstein, *Renoir* (New York, 1958), No. 40; Chrysler Art Museum, *Special Exhibition* (Provincetown, Massachusetts, 1959); The Dayton Art Institute, *French Paintings 1789-1929 from the Collection of Walter P. Chrysler, Jr.* (Dayton, Ohio, 1960), No. 63, pp. 71, 141; Chrysler Art Museum, *The Controversial Century: 1850-1950* (Provincetown, Massachusetts, 1962); Acquavella Galleries, *Four Masters of Impressionism* (New York, 1968), No. 32.

THEODULE-AUGUSTIN RIBOT

St. Nicolas d'Attez, 1823-1891, Colombes

Beginning in the Paris studio of Glaize, Ribot subsequently studied in Germany for three years and later spent considerable time producing copies of paintings by Watteau for the American market. His fame rests largely on intimate interiors of kitchen scenes delicately painted according to the tradition begun by Chardin and Le Nain. He displayed four such scenes at his Salon debut in 1861 and gained wide public recognition. His religious and history paintings, while less widely known, were more that for which he wished to be remembered and are influenced by the Italo-Spanish traditions of Ribera and Caravaggio.

73. SAINT SEBASTIEN, MARTYR

(The Martyrdom of Saint Sebastian)
Oil on canvas, 38⅛ x 51⅛
Musée du Louvre, Paris

EX-COLL: Musée du Luxembourg, 1865.

EXHIBITIONS: *Salon,* Paris (1865), No. 1818; *Exposition Ribot,* Colombes, France (1934), No. 13; *Munchen 1869-1958 — Aufbruch zur Modernen Kunst,* Munich, Haus der Kunst (1958), No. 92.

LITERATURE: Privat Gonzague, *Place aux Jeunes! causeries critiques sur le Salon de 1865* (Paris, 1865), pp. 20, 21, 22; P. Mantz, "Salon de 1865," *Gazette des Beaux-Arts* (1865), I, pp. 504-505; L. Bénédite, *Le Musée national du Luxembourg, catalogue raisonné et illustré des peintures, sculptures, dessins . . . des écoles contemporaines* (Paris, 1896), No. 247; L. de Fourcaud, *Théodule Ribot* (Paris, n. d.), pp. 6, 9, 10, 26; C. Sterling and H. Adhémar, *La peinture au Musée du Louvre, l'école française, le XIXe siècle* (Paris, 1961), Vol. 4, No. 1621; J. P. Crespelle, *Les maîtres de la belle époque* (Paris, 1966), No. 150, ill. p. 102.

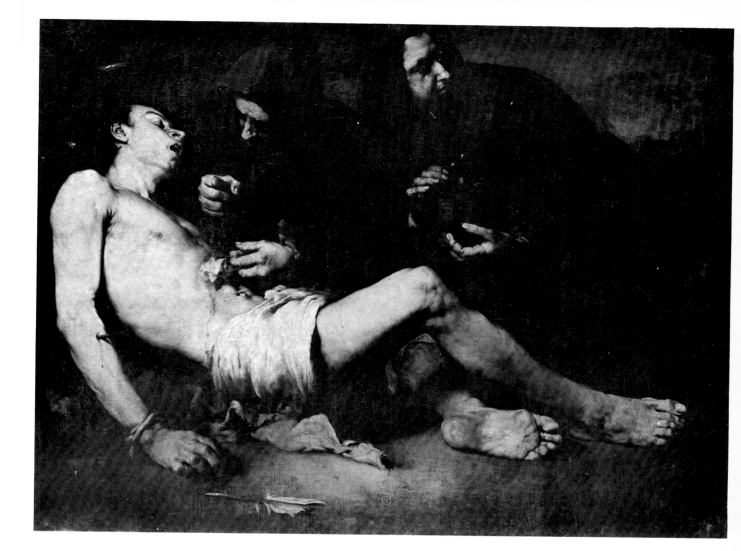

HENRI (LE DOUANIER) ROUSSEAU

Laval, 1844-1910, Paris

Often referred to as *Le Douanier* because of his position in the customs service, Rousseau did not begin painting seriously until his retirement in 1885 at the age of forty. A year later, persuaded by Signac and Luce, he exhibited at the Société des Artistes Indépendants in which he entered continuously until 1898, and again from 1901 to 1910. In 1905 he also began to exhibit at the Salon d'Automne with Gauguin, Redon, and Seurat. Rousseau's recurrent themes were drawn from his own life, but were often combined with fresh and exotic dream imagery. He is primarily regarded as a primitive, and certainly his style typifies that of most untrained, naive artists who represent the world according to their own personal vision. In spite of his lack of technical facility, his innate sense of pictorial design gives his paintings a distinctive charm.

74. RENDEZVOUS DANS LA FORÊT, 1889

(Rendezvous in the Forest)
Oil on canvas, 36½ x 28¾
Signed, lower right: Henri Rousseau
Lent by The Honorable and Mrs. W. Averell Harriman, New York

EX-COLL: Bela Hein, Paris.

EXHIBITIONS: *Henri Rousseau*, New York, Marie Harriman Gallery (1931); *Constable and the Landscape*, New York, Marie Harriman Gallery (1937); *Modern French Masters*, New York, Marie Harriman Gallery (1939); *Masterpieces of Art*, New York World's Fair (1940); *19th- and 20th-Century French Painting*, New York, Marie Harriman Gallery (1941); *Rousseau Exhibition*, Chicago, Art Institute, and New York, Museum of Modern Art (January-February, 1942), p. 16; *Rousseau Exhibition*, Boston, Institute of Modern Art (October 14-November 14, 1942); *Rousseau Exhibition*, Pittsburgh, Carnegie Institute (December 4-27, 1942); *Exhibition*, Toronto, Museum of Art (1945); *Post-Impressionist Paintings*, New York, Wildenstein (April 7-May 8, 1948); *Exhibition of the Marie and Averell Harriman Collection*, Washington, D. C., National Gallery of Art (April 15-May 14, 1961); *Le monde des naïfs*, Rotterdam, Museum Boymans-van Beuningen (July 10-September 6, 1964).

PIERRE-ETIENNE-THEODORE ROUSSEAU

Paris, 1812-1867, Barbizon

Rousseau's family included several artists. After studying with his cousin as a child, he began, at the age of fourteen, to work with the painter Remond and to copy from Claude and the Dutch masters. He exhibited in the Salon of 1830 where his Byronic paintings attracted some attention, and he soon became a controversial figure in French landscape painting. During the 1830s Rousseau traveled through the primitive forests of France and began to paint in a more straightforward and less romantic manner. In 1836 he moved to the village of Barbizon, the first of the group of artists who were to live there. Rousseau won honors at the Universal Exhibition in 1867 but he had little time to enjoy them. He died in the arms of his friend Millet.

75. IN THE AUVERNE MOUNTAINS, 1837

Oil on canvas, 25½ x 31⅞
Signed and dated, lower right: Th. Rousseau 1837
The Toledo Museum of Art, Toledo
Gift of Arthur J. Secor (22.39)

EX-COLL: S. D. Warren, Boston, 1901; S. M. Vose, 1901-1912; Arthur J. Secor, 1912-1922.

EXHIBITIONS: *The Spirit of Modern France 1745-1946, An Essay on Painting in Society,* Toledo, Museum of Art (1946) and Toronto, The Art Gallery (1947), No. 33; *Two Cities Collect,* Toronto, The Art Gallery, and Toledo, Museum of Art (1948); *French Art from 1800 to 1860,* Detroit, Institute of Arts (1950), No. 85, p. 44; *Corot and his Contemporaries,* Houston, Museum of Fine Arts (1959); *Barbizon Revisited,* San Francisco, California Palace of the Legion of Honor (September 29 to November 4, 1962), No. 90, ill. p. 182.

LITERATURE: *Toledo Museum News* (April, 1922), No. 41, ill.; *Toledo Museum News* (September, 1941), No. 95A, ill.; R. O. Dunlop, *Landscape Painting, Ma Yüan to Picasso* (London, 1945), pl. 30; Blake-More Godwin, *European Paintings in the Toledo Museum* (1939), p. 184, ill. p. 185; Jacques Foucart, "Paysagistes et Petits Maîtres," *Art de France* (1964), Vol. IV, p. 348; Denys Sutton, "Nineteenth-Century Painting; Trends and Cross-Currents," *Apollo* (December, 1967), Vol. LXXXVI, p. 487, ill. fig. 2, p. 486.

ARY SCHEFFER

Dordrecht, 1795-1858, Argenteuil

Of German-Dutch ancestry, Ary Scheffer was fortunate in coming from a family with both wealth and artistic inclinations. He was a precocious painter, winning popular acclaim for a painting in the Amsterdam Salon before he was twelve. His ambitious mother, recognizing his potential, sent him to study, first in Lille, then in Guérin's Paris studio in 1811. Later Scheffer became a close friend and drawing master to the Orléans family; when the Duke attained the throne in 1830, Scheffer's prestige was assured. Although he at one time admired Ingres' work, Scheffer was by no means a classicist. Instead, along with Delacroix and Delaroche, he became a leader of the Romantic school. He was influenced by the English Romantics, Scott and Byron, and especially by the German, Goethe. Although he championed the innovative work of Théodore Rousseau, when Rousseau had few supporters, Scheffer's influence upon subsequent painting was slight.

76. FRANCESCA AND PAOLO (Study), ca. 1822

   Oil on panel, 8⅞ x 12
   Dordrechts Museum, Dordrecht

LITERATURE: L. Vitet, *Oeuvre de Ary Scheffer* (Paris, 1860), No. 19; Museum Ary Scheffer, *Catalogue* (Dordrecht, 1934), No. 10, pp. 4-5, ill. pl. 6.

LOUIS-PAUL-HENRI SERUSIER

Paris, 1863-1927, Morlaix

Predisposed by an excellent education toward scholarship, Sérusier began his career by experimenting in theatre, poetry, and obscure languages. Overcoming parental objections, he entered the crowded Académie Julian, where he became an intellectual leader. His Academy-based painting style won him honorable mention in the Salon of 1888, the year he met Gauguin at Pont-Aven and was overwhelmed by Gauguin's ideas. Returning to Paris, Sérusier became a central figure in the Synthetist movement with Bonnard, Vuillard, Denis, Vallaton, and Ranson. Always devoted to Gauguin's precepts, Sérusier's style was, in his own words, like Gauguin's, "impressions of nature . . . wedded to esthetic sentiment which chooses, arranges, simplifies, and synthesizes." Sérusier published *A. B. C. de la peinture,* an instructional and theoretical guide for art students.

77. PAYSAGE DANS LE BOIS D'AMOUR: LE TALISMAN, 1888

(The Talisman)
Oil on wood, 10⅝ x 8⅝
Signed and dated on back: Fait sous la direction de Gauguin, P. Sérusier, 1888.
Private Collection, France

EX-COLL: Gift of the artist to Maurice Denis.

EXHIBITIONS: *Gauguin et ses amis,* Paris, Galerie Kléber (1949); *Carrière et le symbolisme,* Paris, Musée de l'Orangerie (1949), No. 229; *Nabis,* Paris (1955), No. 144; *Nabis,* Mannheim (1963), No. 243; *Gauguin and the Pont Aven Group,* London, Tate Gallery (1966), No. 188, ill. frontispiece.

LITERATURE: Chassé (1921), pp. 22, 31; M. Denis, *Paul Sérusier, ABC de la peinture* (Paris, 1942), pp. 43ff; Agnès Humbert, *Les Nabis et leur époque* (Geneva, 1954), pp. 29ff; Rewald, *Post-Impressionism,* p. 206 and p. 275, ill.

GEORGES PIERRE SEURAT

Paris, 1859-1891, Paris

Seurat studied at the Ecole des Beaux-Arts in 1878-1879. It was here that he first read of Chevreul's color theories. He also studied the paintings of Delacroix whose theories on color were of equal importance to him. Seurat's first paintings involving the color theory of Divisionism were done about 1881; the method of painting involved the breaking down of light into adjacent areas of complimentary color hues. The term "Neo-impressionist" was applied to Seurat and the group of artists around him (Signac, Luce, Cross) by the writer Arsène Alexandre in 1886, the year of the last Impressionist Exhibition in which Seurat exhibited. Seurat became known outside Paris when he exhibited with the Society of the Twenty in Brussels in 1887. Knowledge of his theories and general understanding of his work did not come until after his premature death at thirty-two.

78. PORT-EN-BESSIN, 1888

Oil on canvas, 25½ x 32½
Signed, lower right: Seurat
The Minneapolis Institute of Arts, Minneapolis
The William Hood Dunwoody Fund (55.38)

EX-COLL: S. Van Deventer; Bignou, Paris; Mrs. A. Chester Beatty, London; Paul Rosenberg, New York.

EXHIBITIONS: *Salon des Indépendants*, Paris (1889), No. 243; *Seurat*, Chicago, Art Institute, New York, Museum of Modern Art (1958), No. 138, ill.

LITERATURE: Felix Fénéon, "Exposition des Artistes Indépendants," *L'Art Moderne* (Paris, October 27, 1889), p. 339; W. I. Homer, *The Minneapolis Institute of Arts Bulletin,* Vol. XLVI, No. 2; Summer, 1957, p. 17 ff.; P. Brame and C. M. de Hauke, *Seurat* (Paris, 1961), No. 188; P. Courthion, *Seurat* (New York, 1968), p. 142, ill., color.

GEORGES PIERRE SEURAT

Paris, 1859-1891, Paris

79. PORT-EN-BESSIN, 1888

(Fishing Fleet at Port-en-Bessin)
Oil on canvas, 21⅝ x 25⅝
The Museum of Modern Art, New York, The Lillie P. Bliss Collection, 1934

EX-COLL: The artist; Maurice Apper, Paris; Etienne Bignou, Paris; Alexander Reid & Lefèvre, London; Knoedler, New York; Lillie P. Bliss, 1927.

EXHIBITIONS: *Pictures and Drawings by Georges Seurat,* London, Lefèvre Galleries (1926); *Cézanne, Gauguin, Seurat, Van Gogh,* New York, Museum of Modern Art (1929); *Memorial Exhibition: The Collection of Miss Lillie P. Bliss,* New York, Museum of Modern Art (1931), Andover, Addison Gallery of American Art (1931), Indianapolis, John Herron Art Institute (1932); *The Lillie P. Bliss Collection,* New York, Museum of Modern Art (1934); *French Paintings,* Washington, D.C., Museum of Modern Art Gallery (1937); *Masterpieces of Art,* New York World's Fair (1940); *XXVth Anniversary Exhibition,* New York, Museum of Modern Art (1954, 1955); *Georges Seurat,* Chicago, Art Institute (1958); *Seurat Paintings and Drawings,* New York, Museum of Modern Art (1958).

LITERATURE: Felix Fénéon, "Exposition des Artistes Indépendants," *L'Art Moderne Painting and Sculpture in The Museum of Modern Art* (New York, 1942), ill. p. 75; Alfred H. Barr, Jr., ed. *Masters of Modern Art* (New York, 1954), ill. p. 25 (color); John Rewald, *Post Impressionism, From Van Gogh to Gauguin* (New York, 1956) (second edition, 1962), ill. both editions, p. 115 (color); Daniel Catton Rich, ed., *Seurat, Paintings and Drawings* (Chicago, 1958), ill. p. 89; John Rewald, *The History of Impressionism* (New York, 1946), ill. p. 383, second edition (1955), ill. p. 383, revised and enlarged edition (1961), ill., p. 511.

PAUL SIGNAC

Paris, 1863-1935, Paris

Almost entirely self-taught, Signac learned the technique of Impressionism from studying the paintings of Monet and Guillaumin. Signac was the principal follower of Seurat whom he met in 1884, and was the main publicist for the Neo-Impressionist group. His book *D'Eugène Delacroix au Nèo-impressionnisme*, published in 1899, is a basic document. Signac was one of the founders of the Salon des Indépendants in 1884 and was responsible for organizing its annual exhibitions. He exhibited with *Les XX* in 1888 and 1890. As a painter Signac was more theoretical than Seurat, and his works often lacked the qualities of warmth and spontaneity typical of those by his colleague.

80. BÉNÉDICTION DES THONIERS À GROIX, ca. 1900

(The Blessing of the Fishing Fleet)
Oil on canvas, 29 x 36½
Signed, lower left: P. Signac
The Minneapolis Institute of Arts, Minneapolis
Gift of Mrs. John S. Dalrymple, (62.36)

EX-COLL: G. Pellet, Paris; Max Exsteens, Paris.

EXHIBITIONS: Galerie Bernheim-Jeune, Paris (1930).

LITERATURE: *Art Quarterly* (Winter, 1962), p. 467; *La Chronique des Arts* (February, 1963), fig. 160; *The Connoisseur Year Book* (1964), p. 102.

ALFRED SISLEY

Paris, 1839-1899, Moret-Sur-Loing

Born to English expatriate parents whose bourgeois comfort provided him with an excellent education, Sisley was sent to London in 1856-1857 to begin a commercial career. Upon his return, however, his father reluctantly gave him permission to enter Gleyre's studio at the Ecole des Beaux-Arts where he met Monet, Bazille, and Renoir. He exhibited at the Salon des Refusées in 1863, the First Impressionist Exhibition in 1874, and joined the Impressionist alliance at Café Guerbois. In London in 1871, Monet introduced Sisley to Durand-Ruel who exhibited a pair of Sisley's paintings that year. In 1874, Sisley returned to England, where he painted London suburbs and Hampton Court. Sisley remained a strict adherent of Impressionism until his death. In his landscapes he created atmosphere and space by breaking up reflected color, never, however, dissolving his forms in atmosphere.

81. LE LAVOIR À BILLANCOURT, 1879

(Landscape at Billancourt)
Oil on canvas, 19⅝ x 25⅝
Signed, lower left: Sisley
Lent by M. Roger Varenne, Geneva

EX-COLL: Henri Piedatz, Paris, 1900; Georges Petit, Paris, 1921; Comte de Lanscay, Paris, 1922; Dr. Arthur Charpentier, Paris.

EXHIBITIONS: *Alfred Sisley*, Paris, Galeries Georges Petit (1917), No. 83; *Tableaux de Sisley*, Paris, Galeries Durand-Ruel (1930), No. 23; *Sisley*, Galerie d'Art Braun (1933), No. 13; *Alfred Sisley*, Berne, Kunstmuseum (1958), No. 38, p. XVI; *De Géricault à Matisse, chefs-d'oeuvre des collections suisses*, Musée du Petit-Palais (1959), No. 126.

LITERATURE: M. Gauthier, "Hommage à Sisley," *L'art vivant* (March, 1933), No. 70, ill. p. 116; François Daulte, *Alfred Sisley* (Lausanne, 1959), No. 315, ill.

HENRI-MARIE-RAYMOND DE TOULOUSE-LAUTREC

Albi, 1864-1901, Château de Malromé

Toulouse-Lautrec's treatment of nudes, circus artists, and celebrities of Parisian night life did not recommend itself to those people of the late 19th-century who considered themselves the arbiters of artistic standards. His cold eye and unsentimental approach were offensive to "good taste" and were considered the hallmarks of "bad art." As a boy, he was seriously injured in a fall from a horse, leaving him semi-crippled and stunted for life. This tragic accident and his appearance are coupled in our minds with his choice of a bohemian and dissipated life. Though his life and subject matter were unorthodox, his artistic development was consistent with the progressive work of the last century. He had high regard for Degas, was interested in and influenced by Japanese prints, and was associated with the Post-Impressionists. Through these contacts and interests, he developed his superb draftsmanship and interest in startling composition. These contributions to the development of art are perhaps best seen in his large lithographed posters, made in the late 1890s.

82. TRISTAN BERNARD AU VÉLODROME BUFFALO, 1895

(Portrait of Tristan Bernard)
Oil on canvas, 25⅜ x 31⅞
Lent by Mr. and Mrs. Thibaut de St. Phalle, New York

EX-COLL: M. Tristan Bernard.

EXHIBITIONS: *L'Exposition Manzi-Joyant*, Paris (1914), No. 69; *Great Portraits from Impressionism to Modernism*, New York, Wildenstein (1938), No. 44, pl. X, p. 37; *Views of Paris*, New York, Knoedler (1939), No. 41, p. 24; *Toulouse-Lautrec*, New York, Wildenstein (1946); *Exhibition*, Philadelphia, Museum of Art (1955); *Exhibition*, Chicago, Art Institute (1956); *Jubilee Exhibition*, New York, Wildenstein (1951); *Exhibition*, Los Angeles, Municipal Art Gallery (1958); *Summer Loan Exhibition*, New York, Metropolitan Museum of Art (1960).

LITERATURE: Theodore Duret, *Lautrec* (Paris, 1920), p. 48; Maurice Joyant, *Lautrec* (Paris, 1926), pp. 185, 288; Jacques Lassaigne, *Toulouse-Lautrec* (Paris-New York, 1939), No. 114, pl. 114, p. 166; Jedlicka, *Lautrec* (1929), p. 377; Gerstle Mack, *Toulouse-Lautrec* (New York, 1938), fig. 37, opp. p. 229; Pierre Mac Orlan, *Lautrec* (Paris, 1934), p. 119; Martha Davidson, "Impressionist and Later Portraits," *Art News* (March 5, 1938), p. 11.

HENRI-MARIE-RAYMOND DE TOULOUSE-LAUTREC
Albi, 1864-1901, Château de Malromé

83. BERTHE LA SOURDE, 1890
(The Deaf Girl)
Oil on canvas, 24½ x 17¾
Private collection, New York

EXHIBITIONS: *Toulouse-Lautrec,* Wildenstein and Company, New York (1946), No. 9,
illus.; *Toulouse-Lautrec,* Museum of Art, Philadelphia (1955), Art Institute, Chicago
(1956), No. 26, illus.; *Toulouse-Lautrec,* Wildenstein and Company, New York (1964),
No. 21, illus.

EMILE-JEAN-HORACE VERNET

Paris, 1789-1863, Paris

A member of an illustrious artistic family, Horace Vernet was born in lodgings at the Palais du Louvre which were a royal grant to his artist father in recognition of his services. As the Revolution invaded French life, however, a martial atmosphere came to pervade the works of this child prodigy. Official recognition by the Bonapartist government led to his being named director of the French Academy in Rome, a post he held until 1835 when he returned to Paris. There he managed to survive numerous political upheavals, including the revolution of 1848, achieving a brilliant success during his lifetime. As supple artistically as he was politically, he often painted military scenes in a manner which combined Neo-Classic elements with those of a tamed Romanticism. His career and eclectic style point to a 19th-century phenomenon — the gap between a genuinely modern and revolutionary art and the taste of public and critics.

84. ITALIAN BRIGANDS SURPRISED BY PAPAL TROOPS, 1830

Oil on canvas, 34⅛ x 51¾
Signed and dated, lower right: H. Vernet Paris 1830
Walters Art Gallery, Baltimore (37.54)

EX-COLL: John T. Johnston (New York, 1876).

LITERATURE: *The Art Collection of Mr. Wm. T. Walters, 65 Mount Vernon Place, Baltimore, Catalogue and Descriptive Articles* (Baltimore, n.d. [1884]), No. 101; *W. T. Walters Collection, A Descriptive Catalogue Prepared for "The Poor Association," by a Well Known Critic Connected with the Press, and Sold for Their Exclusive Benefit* (Baltimore, n.d. [after 1878]), p. 14.

JEAN-GEORGES VIBERT

Paris, 1840-1902, Paris

Vibert was the most successful of the 19th-century narrative painters, providing popular works where the subject matter far overpowered any technique the artist might bring to bear. His training was typically that of the Ecole des Beaux-Arts where he studied from 1857 with the miniaturist and porcelain painter Barrias and from whom he undoubtedly acquired his detailed technique. Vibert is best known for his jocular and technically excellent paintings of clerics, presenting in them more "theatre" than art. His happily rare attempts at more noble subjects universally foundered.

85. LA CONSOLATION

Oil on cradled panel, 21½ x 28¼
Signed, lower right: J. G. Vibert
Lent by Mr. and Mrs. Jean Mauzé, New York

EXHIBITIONS: *A Family Exhibit*, New York, Knoedler (1959).

EDOUARD VUILLARD

Cuiseaux, 1868-1940, La Baule

While Vuillard lived more of his physical life in the twentieth century than the nineteenth, his artistic spirit never fully escaped the age of his birth. His style, innovative and influential, was applied to subjects of a domestic and urban tranquility soon to vanish. Absorbed with patterns, he consistently painted intimate views of bourgeois interiors with a broad style which earned him an immediate success when he exhibited in the last decade of the century. His association with the Nabi, Symbolist and Art Nouveau movements forged his uniquely personal approach to painting.

86. L'ATELIER, 1893
(Interior at l'Etang-la-Ville)
Oil on panel, 13¼ x 14⅞
Signed and dated, lower right: E. V. 93
Smith College Museum of Art, Northampton (38.15)

EX-COLL: Josse Bernheim, Paris; Jacques Seligmann, New York.

EXHIBITIONS: *Exhibition,* Paris, Druet (1930), No. 94; *A Loan Exhibition of Paintings and Prints by Pierre Bonnard and Édouard Vuillard,* Chicago, Art Institute (1939), No. 26; *Vuillard,* Washington, D.C., Phillips Memorial Gallery (1939), No. 4; *Art In Progress,* New York, Museum of Modern Art (1944); *Isms in Art Since 1800,* Providence, Museum of Art of the Rhode Island School of Design (1949), No. 25; *L'Oeuvre du XXe Siecle,* Paris, Musée d'Art Moderne (1952), No. 111; *XXth Century Masterpieces,* London, Tate Gallery (1953), No. 94; *Paintings and Drawings from the Smith College Collection,* New York, M. Knoedler (1953), No. 31; *Forty-four Major Works in the Smith College Collection,* Boston, Institute of Contemporary Art (1954); *Édouard Vuillard,* Cleveland, Museum of Art, New York, Museum of Modern Art (1954); *The Nabis and Their Circle,* Minneapolis, Institute of Arts (1962), No. 4; *Focus on Light,* State Museum of New Jersey (May 1-September 15, 1967), No. 109; *Édouard Vuillard — Xavier Roussel,* Munich, Haus der Kunst, Paris, Musée de l' Orangerie (1968).

LITERATURE: A. Basler and Ch. Kunstler, *The Post-Impressionists from Monet to Bonnard* (New York, 1931), ill., pl. 58; *Formes* (March, 1932), No. 23, ill. following p. 240; *Smith College Museum of Art Bulletin* (June, 1939), No. 20, pp. 23-24, ill. fig. 12; Sheldon Cheney, *The Story of Modern Art* (New York, 1941), ill. p. 351; *Smith College Museum of Art Catalogue Supplement* (1941), p. 7, ill. p. 26; *Forty French Pictures* (Northampton, Massachusetts, 1953), pp. xxiv-xxv, ill. No. 33; Robert Goldwater, "Vuillard's Intimate Art," *Art Digest,* Vol. 28, No. 9, pp. 7-8, ill.; Andrew Carnduff Ritchie, *Édouard Vuillard* (New York, 1954), p. 16, ill p. 48.

SELECTED BIBLIOGRAPHY

GENERAL SURVEYS:

Bazin, G. *L'époque impressioniste.* Paris, 1947.

Bénézit, E. *Dictionnaire critique et documentaire des peintres, sculpteurs, dessinateurs et graveurs.* 8 vols. Paris, 1959.

Bürger-Thoré, W. *Französische Kunst im neunzehnten Jahrhundert.* 3 vols. Leipzig, 1911.

Champlin, J. Jr. and C. Perkins. *Cyclopedia of painters and paintings,* 1892.

Cogniat, R. *Le siècle des impressionnistes.* Paris, 1959.

Courthion, P. *Romanticism.* Geneva, 1961.

Dimier, L. *Histoire de la peinture au XIXe siècle.* 2nd ed. Paris, 1926.

Dorbec, P. *L'art du paysage en France, essai sur son évolution de la fin du XVIIIe siècle à la fin du Second Empire.* Paris, 1925.

Dorival, B. *La peinture française.* Paris, 1946.

Duret, T. *Les peintres impressionnistes.* Paris, 1939.

Encyclopedia of World Art. 15 vols. New York, 1959-68.

Escholier, R. *La peinture française, XIXe siècle.* 2 vols. Paris, 1941-43.

Focillon, H. *La peinture au XIXe siècle. Le retour à l'Antique. Le Romantisme. Manuels d'histoire de l'art.* Paris, 1927.

Focillon, H. *La peinture aux XIXe et XXe siècles. Du Réalisme à nos jours. Manuels d'histoire de l'art.* Paris, 1928.

Fontainas, A. and L. Vauxcelles. *Histoire générale de l'art français de la Revolution à nos jours.* Paris, 1922.

Fosca, F. *La peinture française au XIXe siècle.* Paris, 1956.

Francastel, P. *Les grandes tendances de l'art européen au XIXe siècle.* Cahiers d'histoire mondiale, III, 4, 1957.

Francastel, P. *La peinture française du Classicisme au Cubisme.* Paris, 1955.

Friedlaender, W. *From David to Delacroix.* Cambridge, Mass., 1953.

Hamilton, G. H. *Painting and sculpture in Europe 1880-1940.* Baltimore, 1967.

Hautecoeur, L. *Littérature et peinture en France du XVIIe au XXe siècle.* 2nd ed. Paris, 1963.

Hautecoeur, L. and P. Jamot. *La peinture au Musée du Louvre, école française, XIXe siècle.* 2 vols. Paris, n.d.

Hofmann, W. *The earthly paradise, art in the nineteenth century.* New York, 1961.

Jewell, E. *French impressionists and their contemporaries represented in American collections.* New York, 1944.

Laver, J. *French painting and the nineteenth century.* New York, 1937.

Leymarie, J. *French Painting: The nineteenth century.* Geneva, 1962.

Leymarie, J. *Impressionism.* 2 vols. Geneva, 195‾.

Lövgren, S. *The genesis of modernism: Seurat, Gauguin. Van Gogh, and French Symbolism in the 1880s.* Stockholm, 1959.

Mathéy, F. *Les Impressionnistes et leur temps.* Paris, 1959.

Mauclair, C. *Les maîtres de l'Impressionnisme: leur histoire, leur esthétique, leurs oeuvres.* Paris, 1923.

Novotny, F. *Painting and sculpture in Europe 1780-1880.* Baltimore, 1960.

Novotny, F. *Die grossen französischen Impressionisten — Ihre Nachfolge.* Vienna, 1952.

Raynal, M. *The nineteenth century, from Goya to Gauguin.* Geneva, 1951.

Raynal, M. and J. Leymarie. *History of modern painting, from Baudelaire to Bonnard.* Geneva, 1949.

Rewald, J. *The history of Impressionism.* New York, 1946.

Rewald, J. *Post-Impressionism from Van Gogh to Gauguin.* 2nd ed. New York, 1962.

Rocheblave, S. *French painting: XIXth century.* New York, 1941.

Roger-Marx, C. *Le paysage français de Corot à nos jours.* Paris, 1952.

Rosenblum, R. *Transformations in late Eighteenth Century art.* Princeton, 1967.

Rosenthal, L. *Du romantisme au réalisme.* Paris, 1914.

Schneider, R. *L'art français au XIXe siècle. Du classicisme davidien au romantisme.* Paris, 1929.

Sérullaz, M. *Les peintres impressionnistes.* Paris, 1959.

Silvestre, T. *Les artistes français.* 2 vols. Paris, 1926.

Sloane, J. *French painting between the past and the present (1868-1870).* Princeton, N. J., 1951.

Sterling, C. and H. Adhémar. *La peinture au musée du Louvre, l'école française, XIXe siècle.* 4 vols. Paris, 1958-61.

Stoll, R. *Die französischen Impressionisten.* Zurich, 1957.

Thieme, U. and F. Becker. *Allgemeines Lexikon der bildenden Künstler.* 37 vols. Leipzig, 1907-50.

Thomson, D. *The Barbizon school of painters: Corot, Rousseau, Diaz, Millet . . .* London, 1902.

Vaudoyer, J. *Impressionnistes de Manet à Cézanne.* Paris, 1948.

Venturi, L. *De Manet à Lautrec.* Paris, 1953.

Venturi, L. *Impressionists and Symbolists.* New York, 1950.

Venturi, L. *Les archives de l'impressionnisme (Lettres de Renoir, Monet, Pissarro, Sisley et autres.* 2 vols. Paris-New York, 1939.

Vergnet-Ruiz, J. and M. Laclotte. *Great French paintings from the regional museums of France.* New York, 1965.

Vollmer, H. *Allgemeines Lexikon der bildenden Künstler des XX Jahrhunderts.* 5 vols. Leipzig, 1953-62.

Wilenski, R. *Modern French painters.* London, 1963.

ARTISTS:

BASTIEN-LEPAGE, JULES, 1848-1884
Cartwright, J. *Jules Bastien-Lepage.* 1894.
Fourcaud, J. de. *Bastien-Lepage.* ca. 1885.
Theuriet, A. *Jules Bastien-Lepage.* 1892.

BAZILLE, FRÉDÉRIC, 1841-1870
Daulte, F. *Frédéric Bazille et son temps.* Geneva, 1952.
Poulain, G. *Bazille et ses amis.* Paris, 1932.

BOILLY, LOUIS LÉOPOLD, 1761-1845
Harrisse, H. *L. L. Boilly, peintre, dessinateur et lithographe; sa vie et son oeuvre.* Paris, 1888.
Marmottan, P. *Le peintre Louis Boilly.* Paris, 1913.

BOISSARD DE BOISDENIER, JOSEPH-FERDINAND, 1813-1866
Refer to general surveys.

BONHEUR, ROSA, 1822-1899
Klumpke, A. *Rosa Bonheur, sa vie et son oeuvre.* Paris, 1908.

BOUDIN, LOUIS EUGÈNE, 1824-1898
Cahen, G. *Eugène Boudin, sa vie et son oeuvre.* Paris, 1900.
Cario, L. *Eugène Boudin.* Paris, 1928.

BOUGUEREAU, WILLIAM ADOLPHE, 1825-1905
Baschet, L. ed. *Artistes modernes. Catalogue illustré des oeuvres de W. Bouguereau.* 1885.
Vachon, M. *Bouguereau.* 1900.

CAILLEBOTTE, GUSTAVE, 1848-1894
Bérhaut, M. *Gustave Caillebotte.* Paris, 1951.
Wildenstein, G. *Gustave Caillebotte.* London, 1966.

CAROLUS-DURAN, 1838-1917
Alexandre, A. *Carolus-Duran,* 1903.

CARPEAUX, JEAN BAPTISTE, 1827-1875
Clémen-Carpeaux, L. *La vérité sur l'oeuvre et la vie de J. B. Carpeaux.* Paris, 1934-5.
Laran, J. and G. LeBas. *Carpeaux.* Paris, 1912.
Lecomte, G. *La vie heroique et glorieuse de Carpeaux.* Paris, 1928.

CARRIÈRE, EUGÈNE, 1849-1906
Dubray, J. *Eugène Carrière; essai critique.* Paris, 1931.
Faure, É. *Eugène Carrière, peintre et lithographe.* Paris, 1908.
Seailles, G. *Eugène Carrière; essai de biographie psychologique.* Paris, 1917.

CÉZANNE, PAUL, 1839-1906
Badt, K. *The art of Cézanne.* Berkeley, Calif., 1965.
Berthold, G. *Cézanne und die alten Meister. Die Bedeutung der Zeichnungen Cézannes nach Werken anderer Künstler.* Stuttgart, 1958.
Brion-Guerry, L. *Cézanne et l'expression de l'espace.* Paris, 1966.
Dorival, B. *Cézanne.* Paris, 1952.
Fry, R. *Cézanne. A study of his development.* New York, 1958.
Loran, E. *Cézanne's composition; analysis of his form with diagrams and photographs of his motifs.* Berkeley, Calif., 1963.
Mack, G. *Paul Cézanne.* New York, 1938.
Meier-Graefe, J. *Cézanne.* London, 1927.
Neumeyer, A. *Paul Cézanne. Die Badenden.* Stuttgart, 1959.
Novotny, F. *Cézanne.* New York, 1961.
Perruchot, H. *La vie de Cézanne.* Paris, 1956.
Rewald, J. *Cézanne, a biography.* New York, 1967.
Rewald, J. *Paul Cézanne. Letters.* New York, 1941.
Rilke, R. *Lettres sur Cézanne.* Paris, 1944.
Schapiro, M. *Paul Cézanne.* 3rd ed. New York, 1965.
Venturi, L. *Cézanne, son art, son oeuvre.* 2 vols. Paris, 1936.
Vollard, A. *Paul Cézanne; his life and art.* New York, 1923.

CHASSÉRIAU, THÉODORE, 1819-1856
Bénédite, L. *Théodore Chassériau, sa vie et son oeuvre.* 2 vols. Paris, 1932.
Chevillard, V. *Un peintre romantique, Théodore Chassériau.* Paris, 1893.
Jamot, P. *Théodore Chassériau.* Paris, 1933.
Marcel, H. and J. Laran. *Théodore Chassériau.* Paris, 1911.

COROT, JEAN-BAPTISTE CAMILLE, 1796-1875

Baud-Bovy, D. *Corot*. Geneva, 1957.

Bazin, G. *Corot*. Paris, 1951.

Corot, J.-B. *Corot raconté par lui-même et par ses amis*. 2 vols. Geneva, 1946.

Leymarie, J. *Corot*. Cleveland, 1966.

Meier-Graefe, J. *Corot*. Berlin, 1930.

Robaut, A. and E. Moreau-Nélaton. *L'oeuvre de Corot. Catalogue raisonné et illustré, prècèdè de l'histoire de Corot et de son oeuvre*. 4 vols. Paris, 1904-1906. Reprint, 1965-66.

Schoeller, A. and J. Dieterle. *Corot. Supplément au catalogue de l'oeuvre par Robaut et Moreau-Nélaton*. Paris, 1948.

COURBET, GUSTAVE, 1819-1877

Aragon, L. *L'exemple de Courbet*. Paris, 1952.

Bénédite, L. *Gustave Courbet*. Philadelphia, 1913.

Boas, G. *Courbet and the naturalistic movement*. Baltimore, 1938.

Courthion, P. *Courbet*. Paris, 1931.

Courthion, P. *Courbet raconté par lui-même et par ses amis*. 2 vols. Geneva, 1948-50.

de Chirico, G. *Courbet*. Rome, 1925.

d'Ideville, H. *Gustave Courbet*. Paris, 1878.

Fontainas, A. *Courbet*. Paris, 1921.

Gros-Kost, E. *Courbet souvenirs intimes*. Paris, 1880.

Huyghe, R., G. Bazin and H. Adhémar. *Courbet, l'atelier du peintre, allégorie réelle*. Paris, 1944.

Léger, C. *Courbet*. Paris, 1929.

Mack, G. *Gustave Courbet*. London, 1951.

MacOrlan, P. *Courbet*. Paris, 1951.

Meier-Graefe, J. *Courbet*. Munich, 1921.

Naef, H. *Courbet*. Bern, 1947.

Riat, G. *Gustave Courbet*. Paris, 1906.

Zahar, M. *Gustave Courbet*. Geneva, 1952.

COUTURE, THOMAS, 1815-1879

Couture, T. *Méthodes et entretiens d'atelier*. Paris, 1868. English translation, *Conversations on art methods*. New York, 1879.

Seznec. J. *The "Romans of the decadence" and their historical significance*. Gazette des Beaux-Arts II, 1943.

CROSS, HENRI-EDMOND, 1856-1910

Compin, I. *Henri-Edmond Cross*. Paris, 1964.

DAUMIER, HONORÉ, 1808-1879

Adhémar, J. *Honoré Daumier*. Paris, 1954.

Alexandre, A. *Honoré Daumier, l'homme et l'oeuvre*. Paris, 1888.

Bouvy, E. *Daumier; l'oeuvre gravé du maître*. 2 vols. Paris, 1933.

Courthion, P. *Daumier, raconté par lui-même et par ses amis*. Geneva, 1945.

Escholier, R. *Honoré Daumier*. 2nd ed. Paris, 1923.

Fuchs, E. *Der Maler Daumier*. 2nd ed. Munich, 1930.

Hausenstein, W. *Daumier*. Munich, 1918.

Kalitina, N. *Honoré Daumier*. Moscow, 1955.

Klossowski, E. *Honoré Daumier*. 2nd ed. Munich, 1923.

Larkin, O. *Daumier, a man of his time*. New York, 1966.

Lassaigne, J. *Daumier*. Paris, 1938.

Maison, K. *Honoré Daumier; catalogue raisonné of the paintings, watercolours and drawings*. 2 vols. Greenwich, Conn., 1967.

Rey, R. *Honoré Daumier*. New York, 1966.

Rumann, A. *Honoré Daumier*. Berlin, 1926.

Schweicher, C. *Daumier*. London, 1954.

Ziller, G. *Honoré Daumier*. Dresden, 1957.

DAVID, JACQUES-LOUIS, 1748-1825

Adhémar, J. and J. Cassou. *Jacques David, naissance du génie d'un peintre*. Paris, 1953.

Cantinelli, R. *Jacques-Louis David, 1748-1825*. Paris, 1930.

Dowd, D. *Pageant master of the Republic: Jacques-Louis David and the French Revolution*. Lincoln, Nebr., 1948.

Hautecoeur, L. *Louis David*. Paris, 1954.

Humbert, A. *Louis David peintre et conventionnel*. 2nd ed. Paris, 1947.

Maret, J. *David*. Monaco, 1943.

Maurois, A. *J.-L. David*. Paris, 1948.

Valentiner, W. *Jacques-Louis David and the French Revolution*. New York, 1929.

DEGAS, EDGAR-HILAIRE-GERMAIN, 1834-1917

Boggs, J. *Portraits by Degas*. Berkeley, Calif., 1962.

Cabanne, P. *Edgar Degas*. Paris, 1958.

Fosca, F. *Degas*. Geneva, 1954.

Guerin, M. *Lettres de Degas*. Paris, 1931.

Jamot, P. *Degas*. Paris, 1924.

Jeanniot, G. *Souvenirs sur Degas*. La Revue Universelle, 1933.

LaFond, P. *Degas*. Paris, 1918-19.

Lemoisne, P. *Degas et son oeuvre*. 4 vols. Paris, 1946-49.

Meier-Graefe, J. *Degas*. Munich, 1920.

Rich, D. *Degas*. New York, 1951.

Rouart, D. *Degas à la recherche de sa technique*. Paris, 1945.

Vollard, A. *Degas, an intimate portrait*. New York, 1927.

DELACROIX, FERDINAND-VICTOR-EUGÈNE, 1798-1863

Apollonio, U. *Delacroix*. Milan, 1856.

Baudelaire, C. *Eugène Delacroix, his life and work*. New York, 1947.

Cassou, J. *Delacroix*. Paris, 1947.

Christoffel, V. *Eugène Delacroix et le probleme du romantisme artistique*. Paris, 1942.

Delacroix, E. *Journal.* 3 vols. Edited by A. Joubin. Paris, 1959.

Delacroix, E. *Oeuvres littéraires; I, Études esthétiques; II, Essais sur les artistes célèbres.* Paris, 1923.

Escholier, R. *Delacroix: Peintre, graveur, écrivain.* 3 vols. Paris, 1926-29.

Guiffrey, J. *Le voyage d'Eugène Delacroix au Maroc.* Paris, 1909.

Gysin, F. *Eugène Delacroix, studien zu seiner kunstlerischen Entwicklung.* Strasbourg, 1929.

Hourticq, L. *Delacroix.* Paris, 1930.

Joubin, A. *Correspondance générale d'Eugène Delacroix.* 5 vols. Paris, 1935-38.

Meier-Graefe, J. *Eugène Delacroix: Beitrage zu einer Analyse.* Munich, 1913.

Moreau-Nélaton, E. *Delacroix raconté par lui-même; étude biographique d'après ses lettres, son journal.* 2 vols. Paris, 1916.

Mras, G. *Eugène Delacroix's theory of art.* Princeton, 1966.

Piot, R. *Les palettes de Delacroix.* Paris, 1931.

Regamey, R. *Eugène Delacroix.* Paris, 1931.

Robaut, A. *L'oeuvre complet d'Eugène Delacroix.* Paris, 1885.

Rudrauf, L. *Eugène Delacroix et le problème du romantisme artistique.* Paris, 1942.

Signac, P. *D'Eugène Delacroix au néo-impressionisme.* Paris, 1939.

DELAROCHE, PAUL, 1797-1856

Godde, J. *Catalogue raisonné de l'oeuvre de Paul Delaroche.* Paris, 1858.

DENIS, MAURICE, 1870-1943

Barazzetti-Demoulin, S. *Maurice Denis.* Paris, 1945.

Denis, M. *Journal, 1884-1943.* 3 vols. Paris, 1957-59.

Musée Toulouse-Lautrec. *Exposition Maurice Denis; peintures, aquarelles, dessins, lithographies.* Albi, France, 1963.

DIAZ DE LA PENA, NARCISSE VIRGILE, 1808-1876

Claretie, J. *Diaz.* Paris, 1877.

DORÉ, PAUL-GUSTAVE, 1832-1883

Delorme, R. *Gustave Doré, peintre, sculpteur.* Paris, 1879-80.

Leblanc, H. *Catalogue de l'oeuvre complète de Gustave Doré.* Paris, 1931.

Rose, M. *Gustave Doré.* London, 1946.

Rümann, A. *Gustave Doré: Bibliographie der Erstausgaben.* Munich, 1921.

FANTIN-LATOUR, HENRI, 1836-1904

Bénédite, L. *Fantin-Latour.* Paris, 1903.

Fantin-Latour, V. *Catalogue de l'oeuvre complet (1849-1904) de Fantin-Latour.* Paris, 1911.

Gibson, F. *The art of Henri Fantin-Latour; his life and work.* London, n. d.

Julien, A. *Fantin-Latour, sa vie et ses amitiés, lettres inédites et souvenirs personnels.* Paris, 1909.

Kahn, G. *Fantin-Latour.* Paris, 1927.

FLANDRIN, PAUL-JEAN, 1811-1902

Refer to general surveys.

FORAIN, JEAN LOUIS, 1852-1931

Guérin, M. *J.-L. Forain, aquafortiste.* 2 vols. Paris, 1912.

GAUGUIN, PAUL, 1848-1903

Chicago. The Art Institute. *Gauguin. Paintings, drawings, prints, sculpture.* 1955.

Cogniat, R. *Gauguin.* Paris, 1947.

Gauguin, P. *The intimate journals of Paul Gauguin.* Bloomington, Ind., 1958.

Goldwater, R. *Paul Gauguin.* New York, 1957.

Guérin, M. *L'oeuvre gravé de Gauguin.* 2 vols. Paris, 1927.

Malingue, M. *Gauguin, le peinture et son oeuvre; avant-propos de Pola Gauguin.* Paris, 1948.

Perruchot, H. *Gauguin.* Cleveland, 1964.

Rewald, J. *Gauguin.* Paris, 1938.

Rotonchamp, J. *Paul Gauguin, 1848-1903.* Paris, 1925.

Tate Gallery. *Gauguin. An exhibition of paintings, engravings, and sculpture.* London, 1955.

Tate Gallery. *Gauguin and the Pont-Aven group.* London, 1966.

Wildenstein, G. *Gauguin.* Paris, 1964.

GÉRARD, FRANÇOIS-PASCAL-SIMON, 1770-1837

Gérard, H. *Oeuvre du Baron F. Gérard.* 2nd ed. Paris, 1852-57.

GÉRICAULT, JEAN-LOUIS-ANDRÉ-THÉODORE, 1791-1824

Aimé-Azam, D. *Géricault et son temps.* Paris, 1956.

Berger, K. *Géricault and his work.* Lawrence, Kan., 1955.

Clément, C. *Géricault: étude biographique et critique.* Paris, 1879.

Clément, C. *Géricult: étude biographique et critique avec le catalogue raisonné de l'oeuvre du maître.* Paris, 1867.

Courthion, P. *Géricault raconté par lui-même et ses amis.* Geneva, 1947.

Lebel, R. *Géricault.* n.d.

Régamey, R. *Géricault.* Paris, 1926.

Rosenthal, L. *Géricault.* Paris, 1905.

GÉROME, JEAN-LÉON, 1824-1904

Moreau-Vauthier, C. *Gérome, peintre et sculpteur, l'homme et l'artiste.* Paris, 1906.

GIRODET-TRIOSON, ANNE LOUIS, 1767-1824

Levitine, G. *Girodet-Trioson, an iconographical study.* Cambridge, Mass., 1952.

GOGH, VINCENT VAN, 1853-1890

Badt, K. *Die Farbenlehre von Goghs.* Cologne, 1961.

Brooks, C. *Vincent van Gogh. A bibliography, comprising a catalogue of the literature published from 1890 through 1940.* New York, 1942.

Elgar, F. *Van Gogh. A study of his life and work.* New York, 1958.

Graetz, H. *The symbolic language of Vincent van Gogh.* New York, 1963.

Kröller-Müller. Rijksmuseum. *A catalogue with full documentation of 272 works by Vincent van Gogh, belonging to the State Museum Kröller-Müller.* Otterlo, 1959.

La Faille, J. *L'oeuvre de Vincent van Gogh.* 4 vols. Paris, 1928.

Nordenfalk, C. *The life and work of van Gogh.* London, 1953.

Schapiro, M. *Vincent van Gogh.* New York, 1950.

Scherjon, W. and J. De Gruyter. *Vincent van Gogh's great period. Arles, St. Rémy, and Auvers-sur Oise.* Amsterdam, 1937.

Tralbaut, M. *Vincent van Gogh in zijn Antwerpsche Period.* Amsterdam, 1948.

Uhde, W. *Vincent van Gogh.* 2nd ed. London, 1936.

Van Gogh-Bonger, J. and V. W. Van Gogh, eds. *The complete letters of Vincent van Gogh.* 3 vols. London, 1958.

GRANET, FRANÇOIS-MARIUS, 1775-1849

Raoul-Rochette. *Notice historique sur la vie et les ouvrages de M. Granet.* 1851.

Ripert, E. *François-Marius Granet.* 1937.

Silbert, P. *Notice historique sur la vie et l'oeuvre de Granet.* 1937.

GROS, JEAN-ANTOINE, 1771-1835

Delacroix, E. "Gros," *Revue des Deux-Mondes.* Paris, 1848.

Delestre, J. *Gros et ses ouvrages.* Paris, 1845.

Escholier, R. *Gros, ses amis et ses élèves.* Paris, 1936.

Lelièvre, P. "Gros, peintre d'histoire" *Gazette des Beaux-Arts,* II. Paris, 1936.

Lemonnier, H. *Gros; biographie critique.* Paris, 1905.

GUIGOU, PAUL-CAMILLE, 1834-1871

Refer to general surveys.

GUILLAUMIN, JEAN-BAPTISTE-ARMAND, 1841-1927

Refer to general surveys.

HARPIGNIES, HENRI-JOSEPH, 1819-1916

Refer to general surveys.

HENNER, JEAN-JACQUES, 1829-1905

Grad, C. *Jean-Jacques Henner.* Nancy, 1887.

HUET, PAUL, 1803-1869

Hediard, G. *Paul Huet.* Le Mans, n.d.

INGRES, JEAN-AUGUSTE-DOMINIQUE, 1780-1867

Alain. *Ingres.* Paris, 1949.

Alazard, J. *Ingres et l'ingrisme.* Paris, 1950.

Amaury-Duval. *L'atelier d'Ingres.* Paris, 1878.

Cassou, J. *Ingres.* 1947.

Courthion, P. *Ingres, raconté, par lui-même et par ses amis; pensées et écrits du peintre.* 2 vols. Geneva, 1947-48.

Frohlich-Bum, L. *Ingres, his life and art.* London, 1926.

Hourticq, L. *Ingres.* Paris, 1929.

Lapauze, H. *Ingres, sa vie et son oeuvre.* Paris, 1911.

Longa, R. *Ingres inconnu.* Paris, 1942.

Malinque, M. *Ingres.* Monaco, 1943.

Pach, W. *Ingres.* New York, 1939.

Rosenblum, R. *Jean-Auguste-Dominique Ingres.* New York, 1967.

Wildenstein, G. *Ingres.* London, 1954.

JACQUE, CHARLES-ÉMILE, 1813-1894

Refer to general surveys.

LACOMBE, GEORGES, 1868-1916

Refer to general surveys.

MANET, ÉDOUARD, 1832-1883

Bataille, G. *Manet.* Geneva, 1955.

Cooper, D. *Manet.* London, 1949.

Florisoone, M. *Manet.* Monaco, 1947.

Fried, M. "Manet's sources" *Art forum,* VII, 7. New York, 1969.

Hamilton, G. *Manet and his critics.* New Haven, 1954.

Hanson, A. *Édouard Manet 1832-1883.* Philadelphia, 1966.

Jamot, P. *Manet.* 2 vols. Paris, 1932.

Martin, K. *E. Manet.* Basel, 1958.

Moreau-Nélaton, E. *Manet raconté par lui-même.* 2 vols. Paris, 1926.

Proust, A. *Édouard Manet, souvenirs.* Paris, 1913.

Richardson, J. *E. Manet.* London, 1958.

Schneider, P. *The world of Manet.* New York, 1968.

Tabarant, A. *Manet et ses oeuvres.* 3rd ed. Paris, 1947.

Vaudoyer, J. *Manet.* Paris, 1955.

MEISSONIER, JEAN-LOUIS-ERNEST, 1815-1891

Bénédite, L. *Meissonier.* Paris, 1910.

Gréard, M. *Jean-Louis-Ernest Meissonier, ses souvenirs, ses entretiens.* Paris, 1897.

MICHEL, GEORGES, 1763-1843

Sensier, A. *Étude sur Georges Michel.* Paris, 1873.

MILLET, JEAN-FRANÇOIS, 1814-1875

Cartwright, J. *Jean-François Millet*. New York, 1910.
Gensel, W. *Millet und Rousseau*. Bielefeld-Leipzig, 1902.
Gsell, P. *Millet*. Paris, 1928.
Moreau-Nélaton, E. *Millet raconté par lui-même*. 3 vols. Paris, 1921.
Sensier, A. *Millet*. Paris, 1881.
Thomson, A. *Millet and the Barbizon School*. London, 1903.

MONET, CLAUDE, 1840-1926

Alexander, A. *Claude Monet*. Paris, 1921.
Clemenceau, G. *Claude Monet*. Paris, 1928.
Fels, M. *La vie de Claude Monet*. Paris, 1929.
Geffroy, G. *Claude Monet, sa vie, son oeuvre*. 2 vols. Paris, 1924.
Hoschedé, J. *Claude Monet, ce mal connu*. 2 vols. Geneva, 1960.
Malinque, M. *Claude Monet*. Monaco, 1943.
Mauclair, C. *Claude Monet*. New York, 1924.
Rouart, D. *Claude Monet*. Geneva, 1958.
Seitz, W. *Claude Monet*. New York, 1960.
Taillandier, Y. *Monet*. Paris, 1963.
Usener, K. *Claude Monets Seerosen-Wandbilder in der Orangerie*. Wallraf-Richartz-Jahrbuch, XIV, 1952.

MOREAU, GUSTAVE, 1826-1898

Deshairs, L. and J. Loran. *Gustave Moreau*. Paris, 1913.
Geffroy, G. *L'oeuvre de Gustave Moreau*. Paris, 1900.
Holten, R. von. *L'art fantastique de Gustave Moreau*. Paris, 1960.
Leprieur, P. *Gustave Moreau et son oeuvre*. Paris, 1889.
The Museum of Modern Art. *Redon/Moreau/Bresdin*. New York, 1961.

MORISOT, BERTHE-MARIE-PAULINE, 1841-1895

Baltimore Museum of Art. *Manet, Degas, Morisot and Cassatt*. Baltimore, 1962.
Bataille, M. and G. Wildenstein. *Berthe Morisot, Catalogue des peintres, pastels et aquarelles*. Paris, 1961.
Morisot, B. *Drawings, pastels, watercolors, paintings*. New York, 1960.
Rouart, D. ed. *Correspondance de Berthe Morisot avec sa famille et ses amis: Manet, Puvis de Chavannes, Degas, Monet, Renoir et Mallarmé*. Paris, 1950.
Valery, P. *Degas, Manet, Morisot*. Bollinger Series XLV, 12.
Wildenstein, G. *Paintings of Berthe Morisot*. New York, 1960.

PISSARRO, CAMILLE, 1830-1903

Pissarro, C. *Lettres à son fils Lucien*. Paris, 1950.
Pissarro, L. and L. Venturi. *Camille Pissarro, son art, son oeuvre*. Paris, 1939.
Rewald, J. *Pissarro*. London, 1963.
Tabarant, A. *Pissarro*. Paris, 1924.

PRUD'HON, PIERRE-PAUL, 1758-1823

Clément, C. *Prud'hon*. Paris, 1872.
De Goncourt, E. *Catalogue raisonné de l'oeuvre peint, dessiné et gravé de P. P. Prud'hon*. Paris, 1876.
Forest, A. *Pierre-Paul Prud'hon: Peintre français*. Paris, 1913.
Grappe, G. *Prud'hon*. Paris, 1958.
Guiffrey, J. *L'oeuvre de Pierre Paul Prud'hon*. Paris, 1924.
Régamey, R. *Prud'hon*. Paris, 1928.

PUVIS DE CHAVANNES, PIERRE CÉCILE, 1824-1898

Laran, J. and A. Michel. *Puvis de Chavannes*. Philadelphia, 1912.
Mauclair, C. *Puvis de Chavannes*. Paris, 1928.
Riotor, L. *Puvis de Chavannes*. Paris, n.d.
Werth, L. *Puvis de Chavannes*. Paris, 1926.

RAVIER, AUGUSTE FRANÇOIS, 1814-1895

Thiollier, F. *Auguste Ravier, peintre*. St. Etienne, 1889.

REDON, ODILON, 1840-1916

Bacou, R. *Odilon Redon*. 2 vols. Geneva, 1956.
Berger, K. *Odilon Redon. Fantasy and colour*. New York, 1965.
Mellerio, A. *Odilon Redon, peintre, dessinateur, et graveur*. Paris, 1923.
Redon, O. *À soi-même, journal (1867-1915); notes sur la vie, l'art et les artistes*. Paris, 1922.
Roger-Marx, C. *Odilon Redon*. Paris, 1925.
Sandström, S. *Le monde imaginaire d'Odilon Redon: Étude iconologique*. New York, 1955.
The Museum of Modern Art. *Redon/Moreau/Bresdin*. New York, 1961.

REGNAULT, JEAN-BAPTISTE, 1754-1829

Refer to general surveys.

RENOIR, PIERRE-AUGUSTE, 1841-1919

Baudot, J. *Renoir. Ses amis, ses modèles*. Paris, 1949.
Coquiot, G. *Renoir*. Paris, 1925.
Drucker, M. *Renoir*. Paris, 1944.
Duret, T. *Renoir*. New York, 1937.
Meier-Graefe, J. *Renoir*. Leipzig, 1929.
Pach, W. *Pierre-Auguste Renoir*. New York, 1950.
Pach, W. *Renoir*. New York, Paris, 1958.
Perruchot, H. *La vie de Renoir*. Paris, 1964.
Renoir, J. *Renoir, my father*. Boston, 1962.
Rivière, G. *Renoir et ses amis*. Paris, 1921.
Rouart, D. *Renoir*. Geneva, 1954.
Vollard, A. *Renoir, an intimate record*. New York, 1934.

RIBOT, AUGUSTIN THÉODULE, 1823-1891

Fourcaud, L. de. *Théodule Ribot*. Paris, 1885.

ROUSSEAU, HENRI JULIEN, 1844-1910

Bouret, J. *Henri Rousseau.* Neuchatel, 1961.
Certigny, H. *La vérité sur le douanier Rousseau.* Paris, 1961.
Courthion, P. *Henri Rousseau , le douanier.* Geneva, 1944.
Grey, R. *Henri Rousseau.* Paris, 1943.
Rich, D. *Henri Rousseau.* Paris, 1943.
Uhde, W. *Henri Rousseau.* Dresden, 1921.
Vallier, D. *Henri Rousseau.* New York, 1964.

ROUSSEAU, PIERRE-ÉTIENNE-THÉODORE, 1812-1867

Dorbec, P. *Théodore Rousseau.* Leipzig, 1902.
Sensier, A. *Souvenirs sur T. Rousseau.* Paris, 1872.

SCHEFFER, ARY

Etex, A. *Ary Scheffer.* Paris, 1859.
Hofstede de Groot, P. *Het eigenaardige van Ary Scheffer.* Berlin, 1861.
Vitee, L. *Oeuvre de Ary Scheffer.* Paris, 1860.

SÉRUSIER, LOUIS PAUL HENRI, 1863-1927

Refer to general surveys.

SEURAT, GEORGES, 1859-1891

Blunt, A. *Seurat.* New York, 1965.
Dorra, H. and J. Rewald. *Seurat. L'oeuvre peint, biographie, et catalogue critique.* Paris, 1959.
Hauke, C. *Seurat et son oeuvre.* 2 vols. Paris, 1961.
Homer, W. *Seurat and the science of painting.* Cambridge, Mass., 1964.
Laprade, J. *Georges Seurat.* Monaco, 1945.
Rewald, J. *Georges Seurat.* 2nd rev. ed. New York, 1946.
Russell, J. *Seurat.* New York, 1965.
Chicago. Art Institute. *Seurat. Paintings and drawings.* 1958.

SIGNAC, PAUL, 1863-1935

Besson, G. *Paul Signac.* Paris, 1935.
Cousturier, L. *Signac.* Paris, 1922.
Lemoyne de Forges, M. *Signac.* Paris, 1963.

SISLEY, ALFRED, 1839-1899

Daulte, F. *Sisley. Catalogue raisonné de l'oeuvre peint.* Paris, 1959.
Geffroy, G. *Sisley.* Paris, 1927.

TOULOUSE-LAUTREC, HENRI DE, 1854-1901

Cooper, D. *Henri de Toulouse-Lautrec.* New York, 1956.
Coquiot, G. *Lautrec; ou, Quinze ans de moeurs parisiennes, 1885-1900.* Paris, 1921.
Duret, T. *Lautrec.* Paris, 1920.
Huisman, P. and M. Dortu. *Lautrec by Lautrec.* New York, 1964.
Jedlicka, G. *Henri de Toulouse-Lautrec.* Zurich, 1943.
Jourdain, F., and J. Adhémar. *Lautrec.* Paris, 1952.
Joyant, M. *Henri de Toulouse-Lautrec, 1864-1901.* 2 vols. Paris, 1926-27.
Mack, G. *Toulouse-Lautrec.* New York, 1938.
Perruchot, H. *Lautrec.* Cleveland, 1961.

VERNET, ÉMILE-JEAN-HORACE, 1789-1863

Blanc, C. *Une famille d'artistes, les trois Vernet: Joseph, Carle, Horace.* Paris, 1898.
Rees, L. *Horace Vernet and Paul Delaroche.* London, 1880.

VUILLARD, ÉDOUARD, 1868-1940

Chastel, A. *Vuillard, 1868-1940.* Paris, 1946.
Ritchie, A. *Édouard Vuillard.* New York, 1954.
Roger-Marx, C. *L'oeuvre gravé de Vuillard.* Monte Carlo, 1948.
Salomon, J. *Auprès de Vuillard.* Paris, 1953.

5,000 copies were printed by Kolorpress, Inc.
on 80 lb. Cameo Dull; cover, .010 Lusterkote.
The type was set in Melior linotype by Dahl & Curry, Inc.